Poli

One of the greatest achievements of the twentieth century has been to add over 20 years to the average life expectancy (at birth) of British people. To survive into 'old age' is no longer a bonus for a small minority of people but an experience common to the majority. Retired people now constitute one-fifth of the population of the United Kingdom. *Policy Studies in Ageing* is a series of monographs which seeks to promote substantial contributions to public debate about policy issues which affect older members of society. The subjects to be covered in this series include not only the traditional concerns of policy makers with health, housing and social services for older age g‍‍ but also wider aspects of policy such as retirement, income ‍e, education and the use of leisure. These monographs are ‍‍ ‍‍e for Policy on Ageing, a registered charity ‍‍ promote better policies for old people.

‍‍Ageing is aimed at a wide readership amongst those ‍‍ocal government, the health authorities and voluntary ‍‍ are responsible for the formulation of policy or its ‍‍tion in practice. The series will also be of interest to those ‍‍ocial policy or administration in universities and polytech-‍‍ it is hoped, to all who take an intelligent interest in the ‍‍ty of their own later years.

fessor R.A.B. Leaper
mer Chairman, Advisory Council, Centre for Policy on Ageing

titles in the series
‍n Norman, *Mental illness in old age: meeting the challenge.* Policy ‍ in Ageing no 1, 1982

lidwinter, *Age is opportunity: education and older people.* Policy ‍n Ageing no 2, 1982

Jorman, *Triple jeopardy: growing old in a second homeland.* ‍dies in Ageing no 3, 1985

‍winter, *The wage of retirement: the case for a new pensions* Policy Studies in Ageing no 4, 1985

‍ton, Bryan Stoten and Hedley Taylor, *Councils of care: ‍ing a local government strategy for older people.* Policy Studies in Ageing no 5, 1986

Hedley Taylor, *Growing old together: elderly owner-occupiers and their housing.* Policy Studies in Ageing no 6, 1986

Alison Norman, *Severe dementia: the provision of longstay care.* Policy Studies in Ageing no 7, 1987

Policy Studies in Ageing
no 8

Caring by

day:

a study of

day care services

for older people

Susan Tester

Centre for Policy on Ageing

First published in 1989 by the
Centre for Policy on Ageing
25-31 Ironmonger Row
London EC1V 3QP

© 1989 Centre for Policy on Ageing

British Library Cataloguing in Publication Data
Tester, Susan
    Caring by day; a study of day care services for older people.
    (Policy studies in aging; no 8)
    1. Great Britain. Old persons. Day care
    I. Title   II. Centre for Policy on Aging
    326.6

    ISBN 0-904139-72-7

Printed in Great Britain by Henry Ling Ltd., at the Dorset Press, Dorchester, Dorset.

Contents

Acknowledgements

We are grateful to the Department of Health for financial support for this study, to Michael Skinner of the community services division for his interest in its progress, and to officers in the statistics and other divisions for their helpful information. The study could not have been completed without the cooperation of all those officers of social services departments and health authorities who sent information in response to our request. We greatly appreciate the efforts made to supply us with statistics and relevant documents. Thanks are also due to the officers of national voluntary organisations, and in particular to Barbara Meredith of Age Concern England, for information on local day centres run by voluntary agencies.

We should like to thank participants at the seminar held at the Centre for Policy on Ageing (CPA) in June 1987, and all those who organised and participated in the south west region workshop in Exeter in December 1987. Their contributions and discussions were most valuable in focusing our attention on salient issues. We are also extremely grateful to the officers, staff and users of the case study day units for allowing us to visit and observe day care services in operation and for answering our many questions.

The study was carried out under the direction of Eric Midwinter whose guidance and contributions were much appreciated. We are very grateful for the comments of members of CPA's Advisory Council whose constructive criticism was most valuable in preparing the final report. Many colleagues at CPA have contributed in various ways to the study. Thanks are due to all of them and in particular to Elizabeth Meade for carrying out some of the fieldwork visits for the case studies, to Louise Tulip for her meticulous editing, to Gillian Crosby and Helen Monypenny for their assistance with the literature and references, and to Judith Statt for providing secretarial support and producing successive drafts of the study.

1 Introduction

Rationale for the study

Day care services have kept a very low profile in the sphere of health and welfare provision for older people. This is surprising since the number of day care units has escalated in the past 25 years. Day care is not, however, a single, coordinated service. The types and purposes of day care for older people, as currently defined, run a wide gamut from community-oriented leisure amenities for fit elderly people to day hospitals for those who are mentally ill. Day care services in England and Wales are offered by district health authorities (DHAs), social services departments (SSDs) and voluntary and private organisations, with little collaboration between them. It is thus difficult, even for those immediately concerned, to conceive of day care as an entity.

Further, the rapid growth of day care services has outpaced both the debate about their aims and merit and any proper evaluation of their effectiveness. The maze of issues engendered by this developing form of provision has remained largely unexplored by policy makers or service providers. Only recently have some local and health authorities begun to review this comparatively unknown sector of their services for older people in the community. It seems inevitable, however, that day care services will receive more attention in the coming years, particularly if the Griffiths report recommendations are implemented.[1]

The present study was initiated as a timely approach to reconsidering this whole question, to clarifying the complexity of issues surrounding day care services for older people, and to developing policies for these services in the 1990s.

The origins of day care services and policies

The present lack of clarity about day care stems partly from the largely unplanned growth of the different services. *Day hospitals* began somewhat earlier than day centres and originated in 1946 in psychiatric day hospitals so that, as Tom Arie said, 'Day care is one of psychiatry's gifts to medicine'.[2] The concept of the geriatric day hospital evolved in the 1950s when elderly people discharged from geriatric wards began to attend the ward or occupational therapy department for the day. In 1958 the first purpose-built geriatric day hospital was opened at Cowley Road Hospital in Oxford.

From these early beginnings day hospitals expanded rapidly during the 1960s and 1970s until most geriatric departments had established a day unit and some areas had opened specialist psychogeriatric day hospitals. As Brocklehurst and Tucker pointed out, this development of day hospitals was not planned but, like Topsy, 'just grew' and became an accepted part of the National Health Service.[3] Guidelines issued in 1971 in response to this development suggested two geriatric day hospital places and two psychogeriatric day hospital places per 1,000 elderly people.[4]

There was some, although not much, reference to day hospitals in the governmental policy documents of the last decade. *The way forward* (1977) mentioned day hospitals as part of the range of community care services and, as a response to the 'burden' of increasing numbers of elderly people, noted that 'additional transport will be needed to cope with the increased provision of day care, including geriatric day hospitals'.[5] The guidelines quoted in *The way forward* were 2.7 non-psychiatric day patients and 2 to 3 elderly severely mentally infirm day patients per 1,000 over 65s.[6] More recent guidelines for day hospitals for elderly people who are mentally ill, proposed in *The rising tide* (1982), were 110 day places for a typical district with 30,000 people over 65 years old: 90 places would be for people with dementia and 20 for those with functional mental illness.[7]

The white paper *Growing older* (1981) recognised the advantages of day hospitals for earlier discharge from, or prevention of admission to hospital.[8] This paper, however, voiced some anxieties about day hospitals. It raised the question of overlap between day hospital and day centre services and pointed out difficulties over the availability of suitable staff and transport. The document concluded: 'Health authorities need, therefore, to review the functioning of day hospital provision in their areas, in consultation with local authorities, to consider ways in which it might be used more effectively'.[9]

Turning to *day centres* for elderly people, those run by voluntary organisations evolved, as did meals on wheels services, from the work of the Women's Voluntary Service in feeding the population during the second world war. After the war the Women's Royal Voluntary Service (WRVS) continued the role of providing hot meals, and focused on elderly people at home, or in lunch clubs and day centres. In the statutory sector, the numbers of local authority day centres increased rapidly in the 1970s, partly as a result of the establishment of social services departments in 1972, and partly because legislation had given approval for local authorities to make arrangements for this service to be provided, either directly or by supporting the voluntary sector.

Local authorities already had the power, under section 29 of the National Assistance Act 1948, to make arrangements for promoting the welfare of people who were 'substantially and permanently handicapped', which included many elderly people. This power was extended more specifically to day centres by a circular in 1974 in which authorities were directed to provide for such handicapped people, at centres or elsewhere, facilities for 'social rehabilitation and adjustment to disability' and for 'occupational, social, cultural and recreational activities'.[10]

Other provisions for day centres were made under section 45 of the Health Services and Public Health Act 1968, which gave local authorities the power to promote the welfare of elderly people. A circular issued in 1971 gave approval for arrangements to provide meals and recreation in the home and elsewhere for elderly people who were not handicapped.[11] A later circular concerning the prevention of mental disorder directed local authorities to make arrangements to provide centres or other facilities for the training or occupation of people with mental disorder and approved of the provision of meals and social activities at such centres.[12]

Although day centres for elderly people, including those with physical or mental disabilities, were given government approval by such legislative provisions, little guidance on these services was offered in official policy documents. *The way forward* made brief references to day centres, as to day hospitals, and quoted guidelines of 3 to 4 places per 1,000 people aged over 65, compared with 2.6 places available at that time.[13] *Care in action* (1981) referred to the contribution of voluntary organisations to day care but did not discuss day centres or hospitals at all.[14]

In *Growing older* day centres were mentioned as part of a range of services from SSDs, and the provision of day care in old people's homes was cited as an important way of relieving family carers.[15]

An Audit Commission report on social services for elderly people (1985) suggested that day centre services could be managed more effectively, with more attention to the objectives of the service and to liaison with other agencies; in particular the report considered transport costs to be wasteful and suggested that authorities review transport arrangements for day care to identify possible savings or increased utilisation of present capacity.[16] After another Audit Commission report criticising the community care services[17], Sir Roy Griffiths was asked to review community care policies.

The Griffiths report recommended that local social services authorities should arrange packages of care, including day care, for individuals.[18] Funds would be transferred from central government, health authorities and social security to allow local authorities to take financial responsibility for community care. At present a considerable amount of social security finance goes into private and voluntary residential care. Under Griffiths' proposals a social services authority might decide that residential care was inappropriate for an individual and use its community care funds to arrange other services: 'It will need therefore to consider whether, for instance, a significant input of domiciliary care, day care and help to use leisure time would be a better option'.[19] There could thus be an increase in use of and funding for day care services.

The increase in day care services
In her study of day units for adults in England and Wales, Jan Carter estimated that the numbers had increased from 200 in 1959 to 2,600 in 1976.[20] Of these day units 39% were for elderly people and 4% for the elderly mentally confused. Carter estimated that one-third of day units for elderly people were provided by social services departments, one-third by voluntary organisations, and over a quarter by health authorities; for elderly mentally confused people most day units were provided by health authorities.

The growth of geriatric *day hospitals* is documented from surveys. Brocklehurst found that in the ten years from 1959 to

1969 the number of geriatric day hospitals in the United Kingdom increased from nine to 90.[21] From a survey in 1977 Brocklehurst and Tucker estimated that there were in Great Britain at that time 302 geriatric day hospitals.[22] The average daily number of regular day patients in geriatrics in England and Wales, as estimated by the Audit Commission, rose from 4,079 in 1974 to 6,964 in 1984.[23] Published government statistics on day hospitals do not give the numbers of day hospital units, but data supplied by Department of Health and Social Security (DHSS) statisticians show that in England in 1986 there were 445 geriatric day hospitals, and 184 psychogeriatric day hospitals, with a total of 551 geriatric and/or psychogeriatric day hospitals. Total attendances of geriatric regular day patients in England in 1986 were 1.6 million; total attendances of psychogeriatric regular day patients were 634,000; and attendances at all types of geriatric and psychogeriatric day hospitals totalled 2.3 million.[24] Table 1.1 shows the increase in day hospitals and attendances during the 1980s.

Table 1.1 Increase in numbers of day hospitals and regular day patients in England from 1980 to 1986

| | No of day hospitals | | Total attendances | |
	1980	1986	1980	1986
Geriatric day hospitals	378	445	1.5m	1.6m
Psychogeriatric day hospitals	52	184	0.2m	0.6m
Geriatric and/or psychogeriatric day hospitals	411	551	1.6m	2.3m

The numbers of local authority *day centre* premises for elderly people in England and Wales increased from 240 in 1975 to 541 in 1985, and day centre places for this group rose from 11,649 to 24,036 over the same period.[25] In 1985-86 the actual total net expenditure on day centres for elderly people by SSDs in England and Wales was £44.4 million, 94% of which was on the authorities' own provision and 6% on provision by other agencies; this represented almost 9% of SSDs' total expenditure on elderly people.[26] Statistics for the increase in voluntary organisation day centres are not available. We have not attempted to document the growth of private day care services since there is, as yet, very little information on this topic.

Clearly it is not possible to obtain a complete picture of the growth in day care services as statistics are not collated in a consistent form by the various service-providing agencies. There can, however, be no doubt from the data available that a remarkable increase has taken place in this service in the past 25 years. This study will draw together information from a number of sources to provide an up to date estimate of the numbers and types of statutory and voluntary day care services for older people.

The aims of the study
The overall objective of the study is to provide a focus for informed discussion on day care services for older people and to facilitate policy development for these services in the 1990s. Specific aims are: to formulate a working definition of day care services and to clarify the objectives of these services; to review the current provision of day care services in England and Wales; to examine issues concerning the coordination of day care services provided by various agencies; to set these services in the wider context of community care and the role of carers; to examine particular difficulties experienced by service providers and users; and to determine ways in which day care services might be monitored and evaluated.

Methods
To achieve these ambitious aims within the limits of a one year policy review, it was not possible to use the ideal methods of large-scale systematic research such as those employed by the National Institute for Social Work (NISW) team in the 1970s.[27] Three main methods were, however, used to collect data fairly quickly from a variety of sources once we had reviewed the literature.

First, to assemble as complete a picture as possible of current statutory day care provision and policies from all areas of England and Wales, we sent a *circular letter* to all social services departments and district health authorities to request information. In view of the difficulties which a detailed questionnaire might pose for officers in these authorities, we decided to ask, in this letter, for readily available policy documents and statistical information, together with any comments officers wished to make. Authorities were also asked for information on voluntary sector services in their area, since we did not have resources to survey local voluntary agencies.

Letters were sent to all authorities in May 1987 and were followed by a reminder letter to non-respondents in August. The results of this trawl were very encouraging both in terms of response rate and of the volume and quality of the replies. Table 1.2 shows that the response rate was somewhat higher for social services than for health authorities.

Table 1.2 Response to trawl of social services departments and district health authorities

	Total number of authorities	Replies received	Refusals	Response %
DHAs	200	137	0	69
SSDs	116	88	2	76
Total	316	225	2	71

Most of those who replied sent some form of statistics on their day care services and just over one-half gave definitions or statements of their objectives for the services. Nearly one-half of the replies included details of the services provided, two-fifths gave information about transport issues and developments to overcome such difficulties, and two-fifths included the topic of coordination with other community care services in their response. The smallest category of information received, from one in seven of respondents, concerned evaluation or monitoring of the services. The content of the replies was analysed according to these themes.

Second, in the early stages of the study, we held a one day *seminar* at the Centre for Policy on Ageing in June 1987. Participants included academics, practitioners, representatives of voluntary agencies, social services and health authorities and the DHSS social services inspectorate (SSI). At this seminar, the aim of which was to help us to develop and focus the study, the main issues were identified and the current scene and future directions for day care services were discussed. A further opportunity to contribute to, and learn from, discussion on day centres was provided in December 1987 by a two day workshop in Exeter, organised by the south western region of DHSS SSI, with participants from social services and voluntary agencies from seven counties.[28]

Third, we considered that personal visits and discussions with service providers and users were essential to the process of clarifying the key issues and to complement the descriptions and evaluations of day care provision received from the authorities. We therefore undertook a small number of *case studies* in different regions, using checklists based on those developed for an earlier CPA study on this topic.[29] The case studies provide examples of various forms of day care for different types of elderly users, and illustrate the main themes of the study. The examples, selected on the basis of information received through our trawl or through personal contacts made at the seminars, include a psychogeriatric day hospital, a geriatric day hospital, a purpose-built SSD day centre for elderly and elderly mentally ill people, an SSD day centre in an adapted building, a day centre in an SSD residential home, a rural day centre run by a voluntary organisation, and an urban voluntary agency day centre for older people from ethnic minorities held in a home for elderly people.

In addition to these main sources of data, requests for specific information were made to national voluntary organisations, DHSS statisticians and officers of health and social services authorities to follow up points of interest.

Outcome of the study
The study provides an overview of statutory and voluntary day care services in the late 1980s and a review of the main issues concerning day care for older people. Such a comprehensive review has not been undertaken since the NISW study[30] and the three DHSS-commissioned studies of day care in the mid-1970s.[31,32,33] We cannot begin to replicate such research in a one year policy study. *Caring by day*, however, will provide a basis for continued debate on day care services in the context of the developing community care services for older people which are

likely to undergo changes in the 1990s. In this study we identify the main issues and redefine the key questions which will need to be addressed if more refined policies are to be developed for the day care services.

One major gap revealed by the study is that there is no national forum or locus for information, discussion or policy development on the whole range of day care services. This lack, together with the disparate and uncoordinated nature of provision of these services by various statutory and voluntary agencies, contributes to the continuing low profile of day care services and the paucity of attention devoted to them in spite of the escalation in numbers of units and in expenditure on day care for older people.

The study in outline
We begin, in chapter 2, by identifying from previous studies and seminar proceedings the main issues concerning day care services. The first specific aim of the study is approached in chapter 3 with the formulation of an operational definition of day care services and discussion of the objectives of day care, including those stated by social services departments and health authorities (HAs). Then, in chapter 4, the current provision of day care services in England and Wales is described, and estimates are made for the total level and spread of different types of service for various groups of older people offered by statutory and voluntary agencies. This is followed in chapter 5 by a description of the settings, components and activities of day care services, including costs and funding, with examples from the case studies.

Chapter 6 addresses the issues of coordination between the sectors of provision and between day care and other community care services including those given by informal carers. The difficulties experienced by service providers and users with transport arrangements are discussed in chapter 7, and developments such as mobile or localised services, which attempt to reduce these problems, are described. In chapter 8 we turn to the question of monitoring and evaluating day care services at different levels from the individual user to the national body. Conclusions from the study are given in chapter 9, where recommendations are made for further development and research and, on a practical level, a checklist (appendix 1) is suggested for use by statutory and voluntary organisations in monitoring their own day care services for older people.

REFERENCES
1. R. Griffiths, *Community care: agenda for action*, HMSO, London, 1988
2. T. Arie, Day care in geriatric psychiatry, *Gerontologia Clinica*, 17, 1975, 31
3. J.C. Brocklehurst and J.S. Tucker, *Progress in geriatric day care*, King's Fund, London, 1980
4. Department of Health and Social Security, *Hospital geriatric services. Appendix B: Geriatric day hospitals*, DHSS circular DS 329/71, London, 1971
5. Department of Health and Social Security, *Priorities in the health and social services: the way forward*, HMSO, London, 1977, para 3.5
6. DHSS, *The way forward*
7. NHS Health Advisory Service, *The rising tide: developing services for mental illness in old age*, NHS HAS, Sutton, 1982
8. Department of Health and Social Security, *Growing older*, Cmnd 8173, HMSO, London, 1981
9. DHSS, *Growing older*, p 53
10. Department of Health and Social Security, *Circular LAC 13/74*, DHSS, London, 1974, paras 8 and 9
11. Department of Health and Social Security, *Circular LAC 19/71*, DHSS, London, 1971
12. Department of Health and Social Security, *Circular LAC 19/74*, DHSS, London, 1974
13. DHSS, *The way forward*
14. Department of Health and Social Security, *Care in action: a handbook of policies and priorities for the health and personal social services in England*, HMSO, London, 1981
15. DHSS, *Growing older*
16. Audit Commission, *Managing social services for the elderly more effectively*, HMSO, London, 1985
17. Audit Commission, *Making a reality of community care*, HMSO, London, 1986
18. Griffiths, *Community care*
19. Griffiths, *Community care*, p 21
20. J. Carter, *Day services for adults–somewhere to go*, George Allen and Unwin, London, 1981
21. J.C. Brocklehurst, *The geriatric day hospital*, King's Fund, London, 1970
22. Brocklehurst and Tucker, *Progress in geriatric day care*
23. Audit Commission, *Making a reality of community care*
24. Figures supplied by DHSS, SR2A division
25. Derived from DHSS, *Health and personal social services statistics 1986*, HMSO, London; Welsh Office, *Health and personal social services statistics for Wales, No 4 1977*, HMSO, Cardiff; and Welsh Office, *Health and personal social services statistics for Wales, No 13 1986*, Government Statistical Service, Cardiff
26. The Chartered Institute of Public Finance and Accountancy, *Personal social services statistics 1985–6 actuals*, CIPFA, London, 1987

27. Reports of this five year study include Carter, *Day services for adults*
28. C. Shipley, *South west workshop on day centres for elderly people*, Social Services Inspectorate, DHSS, Norfolk House, Bristol, 1988
29. H. Taylor, *Day care under scrutiny*, report on day care provision in Lewisham and North Southwark Health Authority, Centre for Policy on Ageing, London, 1986
30. Carter, *Day services for adults*
31. R. Bowl, H. Taylor, M. Taylor and N. Thomas, *Day care for the elderly in Birmingham*, University of Birmingham Social Services Unit, Birmingham, 1978
32. P.E. Clegg, *Day care for the elderly in the Metropolitan Borough of Kirklees*, University of Bradford, Bradford, 1978
33. G. Fennell, A.R. Emerson, M. Sidell and A. Hague, *Day centres for the elderly in East Anglia*, University of East Anglia School of Economic and Social Studies, Norwich, 1981

2 Identifying the main issues

Identifying issues from the literature and discussions

How much change has there been in the past 25 years in the main issues surrounding the provision of day care services? The short and rather depressing answer, to judge from the issues identified for this study, is not very much. Difficulties with transport arrangements or the lack of coordination between services seem to be perennial problems which have been around since the beginnings of day care and of discussion and research on this topic.

To select the issues to be examined, we reviewed the main research undertaken on day care services in the past 25 years and looked at reviews of such studies. To complement this overview of the literature, we drew on the discussions held at the CPA seminar and Exeter workshop (see chapter 1), where those currently involved in the day care scene as practitioners, policy makers or researchers expressed their views on the issues that are salient today. Research for most of what have become the standard texts on day care was carried out in the 1970s. Some studied day centres, or geriatric or psychogeriatric day hospitals specifically, whereas others surveyed the whole range of day care services in a country or locality.

A major national survey of day services for adults in England and Wales was undertaken by the National Institute for Social Work (NISW) between 1974 and 1978. Results from this 'national day care project' are reported in a number of publications including *Day services for adults* by Jan Carter.[1] In a random sample of 13 areas of the country, the NISW team examined the day services offered by statutory and voluntary agencies, their facilities, users and staffing, the daily practices and experiences of participants, and the implications for staff training and organisation. Postal questionnaires were sent to all heads of units, and interviews were held with heads, staff and users in a sample of day units. This research was replicated in Scotland; results of the 'Scottish day services study' are reported by Tibbitt and Tombs.[2]

Turning to research directly concerned with day care services for older people, the universities of Birmingham, Bradford and East Anglia were commissioned in the mid-1970s to conduct comprehensive surveys of the services provided in their local areas. Unlike the NISW project, these studies used a very broad definition of day care services which included lunch clubs and educational groups. The Birmingham study aimed both to describe the services provided and to investigate their benefits for users and their relatives.[3] This was done by observation and by interviews with users, staff, policy makers, general practitioners and social workers, and with non-users and lapsed users. The East Anglia study used a similarly wide definition and aimed to map all day facilities for elderly people in East Anglia, study the goals of their organisers and policy makers and then, in an intensive one year study of seven types of centre, to go beyond superficial images and achieve a deeper understanding.[4] This study used observation and participation over a continuous period as well as interviews with users and other groups as in the Birmingham study. The third survey was undertaken in Kirklees.[5]

These large-scale surveys included day centres, day hospitals and other types of day care service offered by statutory and voluntary agencies. More specifically, day hospitals for elderly people have been the subject of several national or local studies. Brocklehurst's first survey investigated geriatric day hospital provision throughout Great Britain, studied five day hospitals in south east England and reviewed all patients attending one day hospital over a six year period.[6] Ten years later Brocklehurst and Tucker reported three surveys of geriatric day hospitals in Great Britain, undertaken in 1977–78 to portray the range of provision and practice and identify problems.[7] First, questionnaires were sent to all consultant geriatricians and all health authorities. Then geriatricians in 104 day hospitals were sent questionnaires about patients, referrals and staffing during one representative week. Thirdly, staff, patients and relatives in 30 day hospitals were interviewed.

Another important study on geriatric day hospitals was undertaken by Martin and Millard in the South West Thames region.[8] Interviews were conducted in all 15 geriatric day hospitals in the region; the 18 psychiatric day hospitals were also included for comparison. The authors had previously criticised the development of large day hospitals and the norm of two places per 1,000 over 65s because these encouraged dependence rather than therapy. Martin and Millard had developed a measure of the function of day hospitals, the New Patient Index (NPI), using the proportion of new patients to distinguish between the active and therapeutic or longer-term social functions.[9] In their study on geriatric day hospitals, they examined how far the therapeutic and social aims were met in practice.[10]

Marion Hildick-Smith studied 1,026 day hospital patients attending three geriatric day hospitals in East Kent during one year from May 1971; this research looked at day hospitals in the context of other local services for elderly people which were poorly developed in this rural area.[11] The study provides detailed information on patients' characteristics, diagnoses, disabilities and attendance rates. Using the NPI devised by Martin and Millard[12], the day hospitals had a comparatively low rate of new patients, possibly the result of the lack of day centres to which patients could be transferred. The findings, however, suggested that the day hospitals' function was mainly therapeutic.

A study of day hospitals for elderly mentally infirm people was initiated in 1979 by MIND to examine the development in England and Wales of the concept of a day hospital for the elderly mentally infirm.[13] A postal questionnaire, sent to all identified psychogeriatric and geriatric day hospitals, produced detailed information on 27 day hospitals for elderly mentally infirm people. A number of case studies were also undertaken.

More recently, a study of seven geriatric day hospitals in South Yorkshire, undertaken by the Centre for Health Economics, University of York, looked at how far day hospitals in the area were meeting their original objectives and how well the seven day hospitals studied met their objectives in relation to each other.[14] The researchers examined 'inputs and processes' and the 'intermediate outcomes' of day hospital care, and the transport arrangements of the seven day hospitals. Although the performance of the day hospitals was generally satisfactory, the report identified serious problems such as lack of awareness by GPs of the roles of day hospitals and day centres, overcrowded facilities, under-resourcing, places blocked by purely 'social cases', and the need for cost-effectiveness studies of day care in comparison with other types of care.

Other studies focus on particular day care units or specific topics and are mentioned in subsequent chapters of this report. The present overview of the main topics draws on a number of useful reviews of the day care literature or issues, published in the 1980s when fewer empirical research studies have been carried out.

From their review of day care services, Goldberg and Connelly indicated three major issues: 'how to integrate day care into a continuum of community services'; 'the effective organisation of day care'; and training and support for day care staff and volunteers.[15] Elaine Murphy asked of day care: 'Who and what is it for?' She questioned whether the services really achieved their aims, criticised both day hospital and day centre services, and identified transport as a major concern.[16] The main issues on day centres were summarised by Averil Osborn as difficulties in defining day care, insufficient coordination and planning of services, difficulties arising from short-term funding, transport problems, the underuse or abuse of day centres, and the need for staff training and support.[17] A recent book, *Why day care?*, examined services for different adult client groups and discussed three salient issues on day care for elderly people: the objectives of the range of services; problems in assessing need for day care; and the relationship of day care to other formal and informal community care services.[18]

The issues emerging from these studies were reflected in the seminar discussions at CPA and in Exeter. At the CPA seminar the main topics considered were the objectives of day care, assessment for the service, coordination of statutory and voluntary services at an operational level, transport problems and ways of reducing them, and evaluation of the services and consumer response to them. The Exeter workshop participants identified five priority issues for discussion. Most important was the definition of objectives for day care in a local area. Second was the role of statutory and voluntary agencies and the importance of continuing dialogue between them. The next priorities were the management and control of appropriate services, and a flexible and coordinated transport service. The fifth area concerned the users and questions such as segregation of active and frail elderly people, and the rights of carers and non-users.

Similar clusters of issues thus recurred in all the above studies and discussions and indicated the main themes for the analysis and presentation of the study data. These themes are briefly addressed below, then considered in greater detail in the following chapters.

Definitions and objectives
A common thread running through much of the literature on day care is the difficulty of defining a phenomenon so diverse in its forms and aims. Day care provision by different statutory and voluntary agencies with little liaison between them is very fragmented, as Fennell and his colleagues observed.[19] Their study classified day units into six types, but it was found that, 'Distinctions between categories become especially blurred where the full range of possible types of centre does not exist'.[20] Defining day care, as Osborn pointed out, is a practical rather than a theoretical issue.[21] It is largely a question of deciding on the purposes for which a definition is required, and formulating an appropriate definition. This issue is pursued in chapter 3 where we propose an operational definition of day care services for the purposes of this study.

Several writers commented on the lack of attention given by policy makers and service managers to the aims and methods of their day care services. Day care is generally perceived as 'a good thing', but as Tibbitt stressed, 'Its weakness is that it is too readily seen as a panacea for problems without sufficient thought being given to the form and content most appropriate in specific situations'.[22]

Two main arguments influence policy makers in favour of day care. The first is economic: that day care is cheaper than institutional care. This is frequently cited in connection with day hospitals where, it is claimed, twice as many patients can be accommodated in the same space as an in-patient ward, and only one meal and one shift of staff are needed per day. Murphy held that 'the financial incentive remains the chief argument in favour of day hospitals', but was not convinced that good day hospital care did in fact save money.[23] The second major influence on policy is the argument that community care is preferable to institutional care. Day centres and day hospitals are consistent with policies to maintain elderly people in their own homes in the community.

Turning to the more specific objectives of day care, there are various facets to their diversity. First, they reflect the different client groups among the elderly population; Goldberg and Connelly found that, 'The aims of day care vary in relation to the perceived needs and levels of functioning of elderly people involved'.[24] The aims also differ in essence or emphasis according to the type of service. The aims and functions of day centres seem to be more diffuse than those of day hospitals. Then within the same service there are different, even conflicting aims according to the perceptions of those involved. Brocklehurst and Tucker, for example, pointed out that, 'The purpose of a geriatric day hospital is not simple and clear cut as is, for instance, the purpose of a family planning clinic. It has a number of quite different objectives; they may apply to different patients at any one time and to any one patient at different times'.[25] Functions and objectives may also change over time as services develop.

A recurring notion in the literature is that of the day hospital as a focal point for links with other hospital services, residential care, and carers in the community. For example, Brocklehurst and Tucker described the day hospital as the 'hub of the geriatric service'[26], and Peace reported that it was seen as 'the centre of the service for the elderly mentally infirm'.[27] In contrast, the day centre is often perceived as being isolated; recent developments of day centres as resource centres for the neighbourhood have attempted to counter this problem.

Discussion on the aims of day hospitals has centred on the 'therapeutic versus social' debate. In the early day hospitals social functions were more important than they are today. Brocklehurst concluded in 1970 that geriatricians considered the most important aims to be 'physical rehabilitation', then 'physical maintenance', and thirdly 'social care' for disabled elderly people.[28] Ten years later there had been a change of emphasis in these purposes: 41% of staff now stated that 'active treatment of patients' was the purpose of day hospital care, 19% gave 'maintenance of patients', 2% social care and 38%

all of these aims. The earlier survey had shown more emphasis on maintenance, which 42% received compared with 19% in 1980. Brocklehurst and Tucker concluded: 'Thus it seems that the policy of active treatment has gradually become accepted as the most important purpose of the day hospital, with a much clearer distinction between day hospitals and day centres.[29]

The aims of psychogeriatric day hospitals, however, are sometimes considered to be different in emphasis from those of geriatric day hospitals. The MIND survey reported that the main functions of day hospitals for the elderly mentally infirm, as perceived by practitioners, were treatment (61%), assessment (56%), maintenance and prevention (56%), support for carers (50%), and rehabilitation and stimulation (44%).[30] These aims are clearly social as well as therapeutic.

Martin and Millard, however, concluded that therapeutic and social functions should not be combined in a day hospital.[31] Nor did Elaine Murphy consider providing social support, even for mentally dependent people, to be the proper role of day hospitals which, in her opinion, should be for medical treatment.[32] This school of thought, then, holds firmly that social support is the role of the day centre. Murphy believed that day centres should not be clubs for fit elderly people to meet socially but should offer social rehabilitation to physically and mentally dependent people and should 'aim to help maintain the mentally frail in the community'.[33]

These questions are taken up again in chapter 3 where we report on the current views of policy makers and practitioners on the functions and objectives of different types of day care services.

Users and the assessment of their needs
Surveys show that at least two-thirds of the users of day care services are women and that the ratio of women to men increases with age. Hildick-Smith found that, among patients aged over 75, there were three women to one man; the ages of patients in the day hospitals studied ranged from under 64 to over 90 and two-thirds were over 75.[34] According to Carter, the oldest users were in day centres in residential homes where one-third were over 80.[35] In East Anglia the users were mainly from a semi-skilled working-class background and were well housed;

one-half of these attenders lived alone, 55% were widowed and 27% had no children; although 58% were housebound, 34% were able to get out unassisted and 8% went out with help.[36]

Day hospital users were the most dependent, according to the NISW study; one-third needed help with walking, or a wheel-chair, and two-fifths needed help with toileting or were incontinent; one-half of day hospital patients were stroke victims, whereas users of voluntary or social services day centres mostly had conditions such as arthritis; one-half of all users suffered from depression.[37] Peace found that people with depression were not usually placed in day hospitals for the elderly mentally infirm, which were mainly for people with organic mental illnesses such as dementia or acute confusional states.[38] The most common conditions of day hospital patients were strokes (31%), arthritis (20%), heart diseases (17%), confusion (10%), and Parkinsonism (10%), which are, as Hildick-Smith commented, 'precisely the ones which may be improved by intermittent treatment and observation' and 'mainly those where physical rehabilitation by therapists and treatment/observation by doctors and nurses are most appropriate'.[39]

The East Anglia study showed that where people with different handicaps or ages were integrated in the same unit, it was the confused or incontinent users who caused most concern to others; the researchers advocated special facilities for confused people.[40] Carter found that where day attenders and residents were 'integrated' in day care in SSD residential homes there were more conflicts than when the groups were 'segregated'.[41] Goldberg and Connelly indicated a need for more systematic studies on this question, while observing that, 'Researchers have produced some evidence to suggest that on the whole the ordinary users do not like to mix with very confused and mentally deteriorated participants'.[42]

Some writers expressed concern that the poorest, very disabled or very isolated elderly people had less access to day care services than the more active and gregarious pensioners. Goldberg and Connelly found that access to services depended on factors such as geography, the extent of local health, welfare and voluntary services, the priority given to day care services, and the availability of transport.[43] This suggests that it is not the assessment of people's needs which usually determines whether or not they receive day care.

The system of referral for day care varies according to the type of service. Self-referral is quite common for day centres, especially for those who do not need transport, but potential attenders may also be referred by GPs, social workers, health visitors and other professionals. Referral to a day hospital is usually made by a GP, consultant or social worker; the patient is almost always visited at home and assessed by the consultant geriatrician and sometimes also by a social worker. The South Yorkshire study found that over one-half of referrals to day hospitals were of in-patients; this, the researchers claimed, 'emphasises the rehabilitative role of the day hospital' whereas referrals by GPs emphasised the preventive role.[44] Peace noted that elderly people were most likely to be referred to a psycho-geriatrician 'because their behavioural problems are such that relatives can no longer cope and therefore contact their GP or social services department'.[45]

After referral and initial assessment, decisions are made about admission to the day unit. In the day hospital this normally takes place at a multi-disciplinary case conference or staff meeting. Cantley and Smith considered such meetings to be 'something of a ritual' because 'few admissions were refused'; the meetings tended to be dominated by the consultant and social worker who had assessed the patient.[46] Assessment criteria for day hospitals were, according to Goldberg and Connelly, clearer than for other forms of day care; criteria varied widely between types of service and need, and the surveys of day care generally did not 'reveal how criteria of need for day care are defined and how the service providers weigh up the specific contribution of day care in relation to other help'.[47]

Reasons for refusing admission, identified by Carter, included aggressive or disruptive behaviour, incontinence, immobility and confusion.[48] These are just the people with special difficulties who might be considered in most need of day care, and Osborn expressed concern about who did plan and care for such groups.[49]

Clearly, the present system of referral and assessment does not ensure that day care services respond to assessed need in a locality, nor that they reach those who need them most. Tibbitt pointed out that to do so would mean changing the informal and open door aspects of day care services, but suggested that 'when resources are scarce it would seem there is a case for some means of directing care to the more frail and isolated'.[50] Osborn argued for broader assessment by SSDs so that the needs of individuals and carers are considered in the context of the whole range of community care services, since 'day care should be part of a planned programme not a shot in the dark'.[51]

Practical aspects of service provision and management
How, then, does the daily life of the day unit relate to the stated objectives and to the needs, whether assessed or not, of users and carers? Most of the surveys provide information on topics relevant to this question, such as the activities offered, staffing and management, and funding.

In day centres the usual components were a meal in company; social and therapeutic activities such as bingo and quizzes, arts and crafts, entertainment and outings; and services such as chiropody, bathing, information and advice. Carter noted differences in activities between the statutory and voluntary sectors.[52] In voluntary centres the cooked lunch was the focus of the day and there were fewer activities than in SSD centres. The day hospital programme has similar components but also includes treatments. The East Anglia study showed that in day hospitals there was a higher level of activities and these were more diverse than in day centres.[53]

Activities in day centres have been widely criticised as limited, undemanding and unambitious, although there are examples of centres offering more stimulating programmes. Fennell and his colleagues advocated a wider range of handicrafts, more live entertainment and more educational programmes in cooperation with education authorities.[54] Carter commented that few attempts were made to engage users fully in the social aspects of the day, that users were not involved in preparing or serving the meal and that the company enjoyed was sociable rather than intimate, particularly in voluntary centres.[55] There has been less criticism of day hospital programmes, although the therapeutic activities were sometimes considered inadequate or inappropriate. Brocklehurst and Tucker found that patients were satisfied and not bored, and concluded that, 'While there should be adequate opportunity for diversional activities in addition to active treatment, there should also be time for quiet contemplation'.[56]

There are a number of obstacles to the improvement of day care programmes. Day centres and day hospitals often lack resources, facilities and equipment. Staff attitudes may militate against the introduction of new ideas, and reflect, as Carter said, 'wider social values which emphasise the peripheral and essentially passive role of old age'.[57] Tibbitt argued for more experimental projects to evaluate day centre activities and discover the meanings attached to them.[58]

Much, then, depends on day care staff, their attitudes, and the training and support they receive. The NISW survey showed that three-quarters of staff were women, two-thirds were married and the others mainly widowed; volunteers in voluntary day centres were mostly over 70, whereas SSD centre staff were mainly in their fifties and day hospital staff in their forties.[59] There were differences of opinion on the role of volunteers. For example, Goldberg and Connelly considered volunteer input appropriate to all aspects of care even for the very dependent[60], whereas Fennell and his colleagues thought that such people needed skilled help while volunteers were most appropriate for providing extra services.[61]

There were many complaints of lack of staff, especially in day hospitals where shortages of remedial staff caused particular difficulties. Martin and Millard pointed out that staffing levels were inadequate to give the treatment which was a main objective of day hospitals.[62] Their survey found that there was less than ten minutes of occupational therapy time per attender per day at nearly one-quarter of day hospitals, and at one-third of units there was less than ten minutes of physiotherapy per attender. In contrast over one-half of the units had more than 1 ½ hours of nursing time per day per patient. Day hospitals were found to be largely 'nurse-oriented', but the researchers commented that if the objective of day hospitals was therapeutic, the majority of staff should be therapists.

Lack of staff training and support was widely identified as a problem. Day centre staff generally had little training although they had experience and enthusiasm. They were professionally isolated and rarely had any contact with other local day units. Day hospital staff were usually trained and qualified, but not necessarily in work with elderly patients.

The role of central management, particularly in SSDs, was also subject to criticism. The staff surveyed by NISW complained that, 'There is little consensus with central management about what shared understandings underpin the action in day units'. The system was considered too bureaucratic and hierarchical.[63] Similarly the East Anglia researchers found a lack of interest by SSDs in the management of day units and commented: 'Considering the resource investment we think social services departments are surprisingly uninvolved in monitoring, supervising and supporting the staff in putting the resource to use'.[64] Carter suggested a more democratic system with management committees of staff and users in each unit.[65] Fennell and his colleagues, however, expressed reservations about client participation; their study showed that although this was appropriate to younger members, the older and more dependent people preferred not to participate in running the centre.[66]

The effectiveness of day care services also depends on the material resources available, including premises. Several writers emphasised that premises, whether purpose-built or adapted, should be suitable for disabled people. The adaptation of premises was, however, expensive, which was a particular problem for voluntary organisations dependent on raising funds. The survey of day hospitals by Brocklehurst and Tucker showed that staff in purpose-built day hospitals were more satisfied with the structure and layout than were those in the 50% of day hospitals in adapted buildings.[67]

Underfunding of services was a difficulty experienced by all sectors and restricted the possibilities for innovation. Osborn stressed that the unpredictability of short-term funding made planning very difficult for day centres in the voluntary sector.[68] Several writers commented that it was difficult to calculate the costs of day care services, which included salaries, building and maintenance, health and social services in the person's home, and transport. It was also impossible accurately to compare the costs in different sectors as data were not kept in a consistent way or not kept at all. The question of cost-effectiveness will be considered further in chapter 8.

Coordination between sectors of care

A lack of coordination between the different agencies offering day care services was universally reported by researchers. For example, the MIND study showed that, 'At least half of the sample did not know what day care provision was being made by the local authority or voluntary organisations in their area. Knowledge of voluntary work was particularly poor'.[69] There was little communication at policy level, and little joint planning or discussion of the overlaps and grey areas between day hospitals, day centres and other types of day care services. Similarly a lack of liaison was reported between day care services and other health and welfare services for elderly people in the community. Even within sectors, and especially in social services departments, communication was poor.

Further, there was a lack of communication between day care staff and the informal carers who looked after day care users at home, even though relieving carers was a stated objective of the service. This applied particularly to units for elderly mentally infirm people. Cantley and Smith found that although carers were welcomed to the psychogeriatric day hospital and relatives support groups were held fortnightly, 'many relatives were dissatisfied and felt that they lacked information and knowledge about the day hospital and its treatment'.[70]

Most writers stressed that elderly people receiving day care services often needed other community care services as well, and that day care should be seen as part of a package of care. For example, Peace stated that, 'The day hospital should be seen as the second line of support in a comprehensive service for the elderly mentally infirm, providing a link between the patient's home and in-patient services.[71]

In practice, however, the different services which might form part of such a package were rarely weighed up to allow conscious choices to be made between viable alternatives for an individual elderly person; as discussed earlier, access to services is much more a matter of chance. Even within day care there was, as Goldberg and Connelly pointed out, 'no fully developed "day care service" in the sense of a continuum from day hospitals for the treatment and rehabilitation of severely mentally and physically disabled people through day centres for the maintenance of frail and disabled elderly people to social centres serving as recreational facilities for the more able-bodied'.[72] Fennell and his colleagues, however, argued that the idea of a continuum of care was not helpful because it 'tends to emphasise boundaries between services and emphasise distinctions between client groups which would militate against the best use of scarce resources'.[73]

Given such an uncoordinated and unplanned set of day care and other services, several writers offered suggestions for improvements. There were calls for better liaison between the geriatric department and social services department, and for a policy which clearly defined these agencies' roles and responsibilities since, as Brocklehurst and Tucker observed, 'If the services offered by both the NHS and the social services in any area are to be effective, division of responsibility must be clearly understood by all concerned'.[74] Brocklehurst and Tucker suggested that such a policy could be discussed at the health care planning team for the elderly.[75]

Where social services departments were concerned, it was seen as their role to coordinate day care services offered by their own department and by voluntary agencies. Osborn suggested that social services should collate information on day care services so that gaps could be identified and a coordinated service be developed.[76] Goldberg and Connelly recommended the development by SSDs of the role of case coordinator who would liaise with different services and agencies on behalf of individual elderly people and carers.[77]

The need for collaboration is perhaps greatest in caring for elderly people with mental disabilities, and the importance of better communication and partnerships with relatives was stressed, for example by Brocklehurst and Tucker: 'The rehabilitative role of the day hospital could be enhanced by a partnership of relatives and staff, with instructions on how to carry out rehabilitative procedures when the patients are at home'.[78] A multi-disciplinary approach by professionals was also considered essential in this field and Peace recommended that 'every day hospital should have access to social workers and/or community nurses working as part of a multi-disciplinary team in the specialist service for the elderly mentally ill'.[79]

Transport services

The provision of transport is a noteworthy example of the need for coordination between the agencies. The importance of transport services to the success of day care has been fully recognised, but this is one area where much dissatisfaction has been expressed, particularly by service providers. The main problem shown by all the surveys was the unpredictability of the service. The East Anglia researchers stressed the significance, for relatives and users, of regular transport times: 'Unpredictability of transport can undermine any benefits accruing from the users' attendance'.[80]

One-half of all the day hospital staff interviewed for the survey by Brocklehurst and Tucker complained about the unpredictability of transport, and 16% considered the journey too long.[81] Martin and Millard found that journeys averaged one hour and ranged between a half and $2\frac{1}{2}$ hours.[82] Long rounds and several minutes spent in collecting each elderly person meant lengthy, uncomfortable journeys, although patients and carers complained less about this than about unpredictability. East Anglian users claimed to enjoy the journey.[83] One consequence of long journeys was that the length of stay at the day unit was reduced.

Problems for organisers of transport included a shortage of suitable vehicles for people in wheelchairs, and the length of time spent booking transport, particularly for day hospital patients. The East Anglian survey found that the hospital ambulances were also used for emergency calls; the hospital car service was good but not always appropriate and it was found that a combination of minibus and private cars with voluntary drivers was a good system but difficult to organise.[84] A further problem with transport was that it was very expensive.

Several writers commented that although problems with transport were widely acknowledged, services were still planned on the assumption that transport would be available. A more flexible transport system, coordinated by the agencies providing day care, was considered necessary. Both the MIND survey[85] and that by Brocklehurst and Tucker[86] concluded that day hospitals should have a special ambulance service for day care patients only, rather than relying on the general ambulance services. Fennell and his colleagues recommended, as the ideal transport for a day centre, one or two tail-lift minibuses with regular drivers and escorts; they also stressed the important role of transport staff in helping elderly people to leave and return to their homes, for example making sure that the door was locked or the heating turned on.[87]

Apart from improving the transport itself, another approach was to bypass this intractable problem in some way. Martin and Millard argued that rather than expecting patients to be at the day hospital from 9 a.m. until 5 p.m., which put undue strain on transport services, the concept of 'day treatment units' open from 10 a.m. to 3.30 p.m. could be adopted: 'A day treatment unit or a "lunch hospital" could function with two groups of patients, one having a morning session of therapy and departing immediately after the post-lunch rest period, and the other having an afternoon session arriving prior to lunch in the morning.[88] Another type of solution was to avoid the need for transport or for long journeys by providing localised day care or mobile services. Murphy, in arguing for small and local day centres contended that, 'The most satisfactory answer to the transport problem is to do away with the need for it'.[89] Mobile day centres, travelling day hospitals and other such developments are described in chapter 7.

Monitoring and evaluation of day care services
The descriptive quality of most of the surveys is a point reiterated by reviewers of the day care literature. Evaluative studies have usually been of one day care unit or several units of the same type, so that there is little comparison of the effectiveness of different types of day care service or of day care with alternative forms of care, as Goldberg and Connelly pointed out.[90] In chapter 8 we describe some of the evaluative work carried out mainly in day hospitals.

There are various levels of monitoring and evaluation. At the day care unit individual users' progress should be monitored by the staff. In practice, research shows that this happened in day hospitals much more than in day centres. After the initial assessment which, as discussed earlier, was more rigorous in day hospitals, day patients' physical and mental progress was assessed and systematic reviews were completed, usually at multi-disciplinary case conferences. Brocklehurst and Tucker, however, found that 70% of day hospitals did not have patient participation in such meetings; they criticised this on the grounds that patients' and relatives' opinions were important and the patients' agreement was essential to the effective outcome of decisions.[91]

Goldberg and Connelly considered that regular reviews should be undertaken at day centres: 'Regular reviews in relation to aims and attendance patterns seem particularly necessary in view of the low occupancy rates combined with waiting lists and the difficulties day hospitals experience in transferring patients to social day centres'.[92] They also recognised that monitoring was more difficult in the voluntary sector and that social services departments were reluctant to interfere.

Turning to the evaluation of the outcome of day care, Goldberg and Connelly pointed out that this depended very much on how outcome was defined in relation to the aims of the service and that 'criteria can range from fairly specific and objective measurable indicators to very general notions of well-being'.[93] Donaldson and his colleagues in their evaluation of day hospitals looked at different objective measures of performance and concluded that data on the 'inputs and processes' were less reliable than those on 'intermediate outcomes'.[94]

Another approach to evaluation is to measure cost-effectiveness. Martin and Millard observed that day hospital care was not cheap, and they posed questions about value for money, such as, 'does spending money on the wrong type of staff eventually increase the costs?', and, 'could we get better results if we spent the same amount of money on providing another form of care?'[95] It is, however, difficult to get data relevant to these questions. Fennell and his colleagues found that costs were difficult to calculate, benefits differed, and services were not substitutable and were used by different sections of the population, making comparisons difficult; for these reasons the researchers preferred to judge outcome in terms of the effect of day care on the users' and relatives' quality of life.[96] There are, however, a number of cost-effectiveness studies which are described in chapter 8.

Most surveys, then, concentrated on collecting the opinions of staff, users and carers as a method of evaluating day care services. Brocklehurst and Tucker found that 70% of day hospital staff 'thought the patients were not fully occupied but that it would be inappropriate to try to increase their activity'; and that 16% considered the treatment inadequate.[97] Nurses expressed an interest in receiving training in rehabilitative techniques and physiotherapists advocated a domiciliary service operated from the day hospital for patients too disabled to attend.[98]

In Carter's study heads and staff of day units found satisfaction in meeting users' needs and in exercising their professional skills; the work was considered to meet the personal needs of staff.[99] Fennell and his colleagues also interviewed users' social workers and GPs. Social workers claimed to be in favour of day care units although they did not suit all clients, and considered that some saving in social work time resulted from use of day services. General practitioners were less aware of patients' attendance at day centres but considered the day unit helpful in preparing patients for admission to institutional care.[100]

As frequently happens in consumer surveys of older people, users were found to be reluctant to criticise the services. According to Goldberg and Connelly: 'The point most often made by users in all the studies was that day care provided social contacts, friendship and company'.[101] Fennell and his colleagues, who found that 11% of users expressed criticisms, emphasised that these should be taken seriously because of elderly people's reticence in complaining; their users' criticisms were mainly about boredom and lack of activities, and about other users, particularly those who were incontinent or whose behaviour was disturbing.[102] Similar reasons for not attending were given by the lapsed users interviewed; irregular transport and inadequate preparation for the first visit were other explanations. Carter commented that while most users were satisfied with the service they saw the gains from it only in relation to the day care unit and not to their lives outside: 'In summary, the most important three things a day unit offered to most users are a place where one could mix with others, a place where one could promote alterations in one's view of oneself and a place which offered signposts to tracts of time'.[103]

Finally, the day care services aimed to offer relief to relatives, whose opinions were sought by researchers. The gains expressed by relatives included a chance to relax or do the chores, time apart from the elderly person, opportunity to go out to work, feeling sure that the relative was being cared for, and the elderly person's increased interest in life. Carers complained, however, about the lack of contact with day care staff, unreliability of transport, inadequate therapy, and exhaustion caused by the time spent getting the old person ready for a few hours away. Murphy concluded that most day centres failed in providing relief for carers and thought that, 'A real relief facility needs to work from early morning to late at night, every day—weekends and bank holidays included'.[104]

Clearly the studies show that more monitoring and evaluation are needed, together with commitment to acting on the findings of such exercises. At the level of the individual unit, service providers should evaluate the effectiveness of their services from the point of view of users, carers and staff and attempt to improve the services accordingly. At a local level it was considered to be the role of the social services authorities to monitor services which they provide or support financially, to advise the voluntary sector and to develop overall policies for day care by local statutory and voluntary agencies. Then, at national level, Osborn observed that, 'Basic monitoring of the trends over time is needed, which requires a strengthening of central government's annual statistics (plus definitions and guidelines) augmented by other studies'.[105] In chapter 8 we examine the extent of progress in these areas by the agencies concerned, but first we turn to the question of definitions and objectives for day care services.

REFERENCES
1. J. Carter, *Day services for adults—somewhere to go*, George Allen and Unwin, London, 1981
2. J.E. Tibbitt and J. Tombs, *Day services for the elderly and elderly with mental disability in Scotland*, Scottish Office Central Research Unit, Edinburgh, 1981. Also separate volumes for other client groups
3. R. Bowl, H. Taylor, M. Taylor and N. Thomas, *Day care for the elderly in Birmingham*, University of Birmingham Social Services Unit, Birmingham, 1978
4. G. Fennell, A.R. Emerson, M. Sidell and A. Hague, *Day centres for the elderly in East Anglia*, University of East Anglia School of Economic and Social Studies, Norwich, 1981
5. P.E. Clegg, *Day care for the elderly in the Metropolitan Borough of Kirklees*, University of Bradford, Bradford, 1978

6. J.C. Brocklehurst, *The geriatric day hospital*, King's Fund, London, 1970
7. J.C. Brocklehurst and J.S. Tucker, *Progress in geriatric day care*, King's Fund, London, 1980
8. A. Martin and P.H. Millard, *Day hospitals for the elderly: therapeutic or social?*, St George's Hospital, London, 1978
9. A. Martin and P.H. Millard, The new patient index—a method of measuring the activity of day hospitals, *Age and Ageing*, 4, 1975, 119–22
10. Martin and Millard, *Day hospitals for the elderly*
11. M. Hildick-Smith, Geriatric day hospitals: practice and planning, *Age and Ageing*, 9, 1980, 38–46
12. Martin and Millard, The new patient index
13. S.M. Peace, *Caring from day to day*, MIND, London, 1980
14. C. Donaldson, K. Wright and A. Maynard, *Utilisation and performance of day hospitals for the elderly in South Yorkshire*, a report to the Trent Regional Health Authority by the Centre for Health Economics, University of York, York, 1985
15. E.M. Goldberg and N. Connelly, *The effectiveness of social care for the elderly*, Policy Studies Institute, London, 1982, pp 140–41
16. E. Murphy, Day care: who and what is it for?, *New Age*, 31, 1985, 6–9
17. A. Osborn, *Day care for older people in day centres*, Age Concern Scotland, Edinburgh, 1985
18. G. Horobin (ed), *Why day care?*, Research highlights in social work 14, Jessica Kingsley, London, 1987
19. Fennell *et al*, *Day centres for the elderly*
20. Fennell *et al*, *Day centres for the elderly*, p 18
21. Osborn, *Day care for older people*
22. J.E. Tibbitt, Day care—a 'good thing'? in G. Horobin (ed), *Why day care?*, Research highlights in social work 14, Jessica Kingsley, London, 1987, pp 17–18
23. Murphy, Day care: who and what is it for?, p 6
24. Goldberg and Connelly, *The effectiveness of social care*, p 121
25. Brocklehurst and Tucker, *Progress in geriatric day care*, p 173
26. Brocklehurst and Tucker, *Progress in geriatric day care*, p 76
27. Peace, *Caring from day to day*, p 10
28. Brocklehurst, *The geriatric day hospital*, p 82
29. Brocklehurst and Tucker, *Progress in geriatric day care*, p 70
30. Peace, *Caring from day to day*
31. Martin and Millard, *Day hospitals*
32. Murphy, Day care: who and what is it for?
33. Murphy, Day care: who and what is it for?, p 9
34. Hildick-Smith, Geriatric day hospitals
35. Carter, *Day services for adults*
36. Fennell *et al*, *Day centres for the elderly*
37. Carter, *Day services for adults*
38. Peace, *Caring from day to day*
39. Hildick-Smith, Geriatric day hospitals, p 43
40. Fennell *et al*, *Day centres for the elderly*
41. Carter, *Day services for adults*

42. Goldberg and Connelly, *The effectiveness of social care*, p 130
43. Goldberg and Connelly, *The effectiveness of social care*
44. Donaldson *et al*, *Utilisation and performance*, ch 7
45. Peace, *Caring from day to day*, p 19
46. C. Cantley and G. Smith, Day care for the elderly in G. Horobin (ed), *Why day care?*, Research highlights in social work 14, Jessica Kingsley, London, 1987, p 31
47. Goldberg and Connelly, *The effectiveness of social care*, p 124
48. Carter, *Day services for adults*
49. Osborn, *Day care for older people*
50. Tibbitt, Day care, p 21
51. Osborn, *Day care for older people*, p 8
52. Carter, *Day services for adults*
53. Fennell *et al*, *Day centres for the elderly*
54. Fennell *et al*, *Day centres for the elderly*
55. Carter, *Day services for adults*
56. Brocklehurst and Tucker, *Progress in geriatric day care*, p 187
57. Carter, *Day services for adults*, p 150
58. Tibbitt, Day care
59. Carter, *Day services for adults*
60. Goldberg and Connelly, *The effectiveness of social care*
61. Fennell *et al*, *Day centres for the elderly*
62. Martin and Millard, *Day hospitals*
63. Carter, *Day services for adults*, p 325
64. Fennell *et al*, *Day centres for the elderly*, p 207
65. Carter, *Day services for adults*
66. Fennell *et al*, *Day centres for the elderly*
67. Brocklehurst and Tucker, *Progress in geriatric day care*
68. Osborn, *Day care for older people*
69. Peace, *Caring from day to day*, p 23
70. Cantley and Smith, Day care for the elderly, p 35
71. Peace, *Caring from day to day*, p 31
72. Goldberg and Connelly, *The effectiveness of social care*, p 118
73. Fennell *et al*, *Day centres for the elderly*, p 199
74. Brocklehurst and Tucker, *Progress in geriatric day care*, p 176
75. Brocklehurst and Tucker, *Progress in geriatric day care*
76. Osborn, *Day care for older people*
77. Goldberg and Connelly, *The effectiveness of social care*
78. Brocklehurst and Tucker, *Progress in geriatric day care*, p 179
79. Peace, *Caring from day to day*, p 79
80. Fennell *et al*, *Day centres for the elderly*, p 204
81. Brocklehurst and Tucker, *Progress in geriatric day care*
82. Martin and Millard, *Day hospitals*
83. Fennell *et al*, *Day centres for the elderly*
84. Fennell *et al*, *Day centres for the elderly*
85. Peace, *Caring from day to day*
86. Brocklehurst and Tucker, *Progress in geriatric day care*
87. Fennell *et al*, *Day centres for the elderly*

88. Martin and Millard, *Day hospitals*, p 41
89. Murphy, Day care: who and what is it for?, p 9
90. Goldberg and Connelly, *The effectiveness of social care*
91. Brocklehurst and Tucker, *Progress in geriatric day care*
92. Goldberg and Connelly, *The effectiveness of social care*, p 134
93. Goldberg and Connelly, *The effectiveness of social care*, p 136
94. Donaldson *et al*, *Utilisation and performance*, ch 7
95. Martin and Millard, *Day hospitals*, p 46
96. Fennell *et al*, *Day centres for the elderly*
97. Brocklehurst and Tucker, *Progress in geriatric day care*, p 66
98. Brocklehurst and Tucker, *Progress in geriatric day care*
99. Carter, *Day services for adults*
100. Fennell *et al*, *Day centres for the elderly*
101. Goldberg and Connelly, *The effectiveness of social care*, p 137
102. Fennell *et al*, *Day centres for the elderly*
103. Carter, *Day services for adults*, p 279
104. Murphy, Day care: who and what is it for?, p 9
105. Osborn, *Day care for older people*, p 6

3 Definitions and objectives of day care services

Introduction

What *is* day care, and what is it *for*? Such deceptively simple questions are fundamental to any discussion of day care, but have rarely been adequately addressed, particularly at policy and operational levels. Day care services meet a wide range of needs. One of the advantages of this type of provision is that it can be flexible and adapt to individual needs. Such variety and flexibility should not, however, be an excuse for failing to think clearly about the aims of the services. Policy makers and service providers must define the services in order to plan and secure funding for them. Managers and staff need to know what is expected of them and to be able to work within the limitations of available resources. Similarly users and potential users of the services need to know what is provided and for what purposes.

There is, however, a danger in defining services too rigidly with consequent need for strict assessment and loss of flexibility and consumer choice. It is important to keep a balance between tight definition and the need for flexibility.

One of the first difficulties in defining day care is that of deciding on terminology to describe the service offered. The use of the word 'care' is problematic because it has passive, paternalistic connotations and neglects the active aspects of the services, as pointed out in a Central Council for Education and Training in Social Work (CCETSW) report.[1] It could also imply an obligation to provide 'care', however defined. The terms 'day centre' and 'day hospital' have associations with buildings rather than services, and neither can be used as a generic term to embrace the range of services offered in such venues, from social activities to medical treatment. The CCETSW report chose the term 'day services' because it 'avoids prejudice and physical limitations'.[2] Experience during our study, however, showed that this very general term could be misleading as people sometimes assumed that it meant any services, including domiciliary services, provided during the day. We thus decided to use 'day care services' which is more closely associated with services offered outside the home.

Having decided on terminology, there are further difficulties in defining day care services and stating their objectives. First, there is the question of what to include in the definition, since the rationale for each of its components should be given. Then there are the different dimensions of stating objectives: the theoretical or strategic objectives and the operational ones, which in practice are often contradictory. The objectives of the different people involved, for example staff, users, volunteers or carers, may also be in conflict. The recognition that there are multiple goals within one organisation is important for understanding the operation of that unit, as Cantley and Smith found when evaluating a psychogeriatric day hospital; they pointed out that, 'Although such an appreciation of the complexity of organisational goals and functioning has been widely recognised in the field of health and social services, it has not been as fully explored as it might have been in the field of day care'.[3]

Further, the stated objectives are often limited by the facilities and resources available, especially the buildings. Even if it were desirable, it is rarely possible to start from theoretical expectations about the benefits or outcome of day care and build the service from this. Objectives are often derived from the present components of day care, from the practicalities of the resources available and the activities currently undertaken.

Operational definition for the CPA study
Bearing these points in mind, we first formulated an operational definition of the day care services to be included in this study. Previous research shows that the usual components of such a definition are: the setting, outside the user's home; the notion of communal care; the presence of care givers; a number of days or hours of opening; and the fact that users come or are brought and return home on the same day. For example, Averil Osborn's working definition of day centre care was, 'Communal care which has care givers present (who may be volunteers) in a setting outwith the individual's own home and which is open for at least a four hour period in the day'.[4] Brocklehurst defined a day hospital as, 'A building to which patients may come, or be brought, in the morning, where they may spend several

hours in therapeutic activity and whence they return subsequently on the same day to their own homes'.[5]

In stipulating a setting outside the user's own home questions arise as to whether to include residents of old people's homes or hospital in-patients. It could be argued that these should be excluded on the grounds that an essential function of day care services is to help people to remain independent in the community. Residential homes are, however, situated in the community, and there is no reason why residents should not benefit from the day care services provided on the premises or maintain contact with a local day centre which they previously attended. Day hospitals aim to rehabilitate people into the community and in-patients attend for this purpose. We have included such residents and long-stay patients in defining day care services as outside the person's own home, which in such cases refers to their personal room or ward which may be on the same site.

The 'communal care' and 'care givers' components of a definition raise the question of whether to include purely social or educational facilities such as social clubs, lunch clubs or adult education classes. At the Exeter seminar some participants argued that a lunch club offering a meal and conversation could be considered as care, while others thought that such needs could be met just as well by providing transport to a local pub. The question of whose responsibility it is to meet purely social needs was discussed at the CPA seminar. It was felt that day care services provided by social services departments and voluntary agencies should meet wider needs than the social ones which would be catered for as one, but not the only, essential part of the service. For this study we have excluded purely social and educational facilities from our definition and included only those where people attend for most of the day and are offered care in the sense of some form of therapeutic, social or medical attention or support.

Some definitions of day care specify that the unit is open for at least three days a week. For example, Jan Carter defined a day unit as, 'A non-profit-making personal service which offers communal care and which has care givers present in a non-domiciliary and non-residential setting for at least three days a week and which is open at least four to five hours each day'.[6] However, there are, especially in the voluntary sector, day clubs or centres which provide all the components of day care but only for one or two days a week. Users sometimes attend more than one such centre during the week. We have included all such units.

Our operational definition is based on those used in previous studies. The definition is as follows: *A day care service offers communal care, with paid or voluntary care givers present, in a setting outside the user's own home. Individuals come or are brought to use the services, which are available for at least four hours during the day, and return home on the same day.*

Definition of types or users of day care services
Beyond the general operational definition encompassing all relevant services, there are more specific definitions for different types of day care provision. Other definitions consider services in terms of the various client groups which constitute their users or potential users. Alan Norton and his colleagues, for example, identified three categories of day centres: for 'fit or minimally dependent people'; for 'those with heavy dependency'; and for 'those at medium risk'.[7] In their review of day care studies, Goldberg and Connelly found five categories of users of day services: 'the reasonably well and active'; the 'physically fit . . . in need of some kind of external stimulus'; 'those who have completed hospital in-patient treatment . . . but who will benefit from further treatment at a day hospital'; 'those who are physically disabled to such an extent that they cannot leave their own homes without aid'; and 'the confused or mentally ill elderly'.[8]

There is also a question of whether to integrate or segregate different types of user or those with special needs. There have been successful projects integrating elderly people with younger mentally or physically handicapped groups or with children. Elderly mentally dependent people, particularly those with dementia, are often considered to be best catered for by separate provision.

Definitions, of course, depend on the use for which they are intended. For policy makers it would seem essential to define the relevant type(s) of provision, for example day centre, geriatric day hospital, or psychogeriatric day hospital, together with the categories of users envisaged for each, and a statement of whether, in individual units, such client groups will be integrated or offered separate provision.

More specific definitions of particular types of unit or provision for different groups usually include some notion of the function or aims of the service. Day centres tend to emphasise the social or preventive side, whereas day hospitals include therapeutic or rehabilitative aspects. It is important to distinguish these functions in definitions of each type of provision. Another distinction is between the roles of the voluntary and statutory sectors, particularly in providing day centres. The voluntary sector is often seen as catering for the more social needs while the statutory authorities meet the needs which require more professional help. But in rural areas it is often necessary to offer the whole range of care in one centre.

In defining day centres our social services respondents usually focused on day care as part of community care, designed to help older people to live independently in their own homes. For example, Bedfordshire SSD's social centres manual stated that, 'The Centre is the focus for the preventive services provided outside the confines of a person's own home. As such it is an essential part of the community care framework'. Health authority definitions of day hospitals stressed treatment and rehabilitation provided after discharge from hospital care or to avoid in-patient admission. West Glamorgan HA, for example, stated that, 'Day hospitals provide multi-disciplinary assessment and treatment for patients who do not require hospital admission, and are also used for continuing rehabilitation and treatment of patients discharged from hospital'.

Setting objectives for day care services
The main concept to emerge from the CPA seminar on the topic of objectives was that of compensating for a lack. Day care services were seen as filling lacks where older people were unable to organise this for themselves particularly where social or care needs were concerned. But the question arose as to who perceives these lacks and whether they are professional assumptions or the felt needs of older people themselves. There is a danger of paternalistic attitudes and assumptions about dependence and loss of skills if professionals define needs for care. Participants at the CPA seminar felt that day care services should enable users to compensate for their own lacks.

In the literature on the aims and objectives of day care services, the focus is on specific functions. Goldberg and Connelly identified five main aims: 'to socialise, and to enjoy a meal in company'; 'to relieve strain on relatives'; 'functional improvement' particularly for mentally dependent people; 'rehabilitation and maintenance', especially in day hospitals; and 'to offer a substitute for residential care', or 'to prepare the elderly for residential care'.[9]

Other studies identified much more detailed aims for different types of unit or from different perspectives, for example those of medical or social work staff, care assistants, users or relatives. Brocklehurst and Tucker, for instance, stressed that the geriatric day hospital has several different objectives and that these are perceived differently by the various professionals. They found that 'physicians and physiotherapists were more likely to see active treatment as the main purpose than were nurses and occupational therapists'.[10] Carter found that 48% of users saw providing practical services such as company, food and occupation as an aim in day units, compared with 29% of heads and staff; 19% of heads and staff but none of the users gave keeping users out of hospital as an aim.[11]

Objectives stated by policy makers, if indeed they are stated, are thus not necessarily the same as those perceived by staff, users or relatives. It is unlikely that a consensus about the main aims of a day care service would be found among all those concerned. Further, the stated objectives are often not those achieved in practice and the statements rarely give any indication of how the aims will be met. It is, however, important to consider what policy makers perceive as the main aims of the day care services offered.

Although CPA's request for information from SSDs and DHAs did not specify this, over one-half of the authorities who replied included statements of objectives, often contained in documents such as reviews of services to elderly people or of day care, policy statements or plans, or operational policies, particularly for day hospitals. The content of such statements is analysed and presented separately for day centres and day hospitals.

SSD objectives for social services and voluntary organisation day centres

Analysis of SSD responses shows that these fell into nine categories and the authorities' aims were presented in various combinations of these categories, some more detailed than others. The findings are shown in table 3.1.

Table 3.1 SSD objectives for day centres

Order of frequency	Category of objectives	% of replies
1.	Prevention: helping people remain independent in the community	74
2.	Social care and stimulation, company	65
3.	Developing/maintaining physical and mental skills	59
4.	Relief, respite, support for carers	57
5.	Assessment, monitoring, providing individual packages of care	50
6.	Providing basic personal care services	43
7.	Rehabilitation and treatment	33
8.	Social/psychological support and advice for the individual	26
9.	Resource centre, outreach service	11
		N = 46

The most frequently mentioned category, *prevention*, included avoiding the need for residential or hospital care, or facilitating rehabilitation from such care, or from day hospital. Statements sometimes mentioned improving the quality of elderly people's lives in the community; more often, however, the emphasis was on keeping people out of more expensive forms of care; for example, 'Day care is essentially concerned with keeping people in the community, and as independent of our services as possible' (Cheshire SSD).

Social care often included relieving isolation or loneliness; for example, 'to provide a service which befriends the lonely and which should be made available to all elderly people who live alone and are socially isolated' (Birmingham SSD). Less frequently mentioned were providing a point of stability and group identity outside the home, and giving elderly people a role as volunteers and encouraging their participation in running the centre.

Table 3.2 DHA objectives for day hospitals

Order of frequency	Category of objective	% of replies
1.	Rehabilitation and treatment	82
2.	Prevention: helping people remain independent in the community	67
3.	Assessment and monitoring	56
4.	Relief, respite, support for carers	35
5.	Developing/maintaining physical and mental skills	29
6.	Social care and stimulation, company	26
7.	Resource centre, outreach service	23
8.	Providing basic personal care services	14
9.	Social/psychological support and advice for the individual	10
10.	Teaching and training staff	7
		N = 84

The aim of *developing and maintaining skills* comprised physical and mental stimulation, recreational and therapeutic activities, and also promoting positive health and welfare. *Relief of carers* was a straightforward aim as exemplified by Northumberland SSD: 'the provision of necessary relief to families, neighbours or friends who may be the sole means of support in helping people to manage in their own homes'.

Assessment and monitoring included multi-disciplinary assessment, assessment for residential care and referral to other agencies. The notion of an individual package of care was often mentioned, as in this example from Lincolnshire SSD: 'to provide a service which will be integrated into an overall plan of assistance to the elderly person'.

Among the *basic care services* which statements mentioned as aims of day care were providing or arranging for meals, warmth, transport, safety and security, bathing, toileting, laundry, shopping, hairdressing, chiropody, ophthalmic and dental care. Gwynedd SSD, for example, held that the day care environment should 'ensure that the basic requirements of life are being met; food, warmth, clothing and personal hygiene enabling the development of good habit forming'.

Rehabilitation and treatment covered nursing and medical treatment and screening, occupational therapy, physiotherapy and speech therapy, and monitoring the effects of drugs. *Support and advice* included preparation for, or coping with change, such as disability, bereavement, or going into residential care, and individual help, advice, information or counselling, health education and welfare rights.

The aim of providing a *resource centre or outreach service* was least frequently stated but is a growing area of interest in day care services. Examples given were a pop-in facility, use of the day centre by voluntary groups, use as a base for meals provision, and encouraging users' integration within the community. A unit in Derbyshire, for example, aimed 'to provide and develop an outreach service i.e. outwith the unit, both during the period of attendance at the unit, and as follow-up'.

DHA objectives for day hospitals
Over one-half (53%) of the DHAs which replied to our letter stated objectives for day hospitals. Of these 72 authorities, 65 referred to geriatric day hospitals or to day hospitals for elderly people in general, while 19 referred specifically to psychogeriatric day hospitals (12 of these in addition to the other category). It is thus difficult completely to separate the objectives for the two types of day hospitals for elderly people, but some comparisons are made. Objectives for day hospitals fell into the same categories as those for day centres, with one important addition, that of teaching and training staff. Table 3.2 shows the proportion of the total 84 replies giving aims in each of these categories.

As expected, *rehabilitation and treatment* was the most frequently mentioned aim for day hospitals; authorities cited medical and nursing treatment and screening, the management of disease and disability, therapy, clinical psychology and psychotherapy. For example, a day hospital in Preston HA aimed 'to treat patients with medical conditions and improve these as much as possible through rehabilitation and mobilisation, to enable them to lead as active and useful a life as possible in the community'. This objective was slightly less prominent for the psychogeriatric day hospitals. In stating the objective of *prevention*, authorities focused on preventing hospital admissions, supporting hospital discharges and saving hospital beds.

Assessment and monitoring, the third most cited aim overall, was more important for psychogeriatric day hospitals than for the main group; it was the most frequently mentioned objective, jointly with rehabilitation and treatment, for psychogeriatric day hospitals; for example, 'to treat, assess, observe and monitor elderly people with psychiatric and emotional problems as day patients' (psychogeriatric day hospital in Waltham Forest HA). Emphasis was placed on multi-disciplinary assessment and diagnosis.

Just over one-third of authorities gave *relief for carers* as an objective, but the proportion was much higher, over one-half, for the psychogeriatric day hospitals. This category included advice and counselling for carers and encouraging their participation. A Chester HA psychogeriatric day hospital, for example, aimed to 'increase the carer's/supporter's understanding of the patient's mental and functional ability and advise on the management of the patient in the home situation'.

The category *developing and maintaining skills* focused on therapeutic activities and included the aim of maximising health and function. *Social care* was slightly more prominent for the psychogeriatric day hospitals which included training in social skills; for example, 'to give patients the opportunity of making social contacts, to control the effects of isolation and to modify anti-social behaviour' (East Suffolk HA day hospital).

In the context of maintaining links with the community to which patients would be discharged, a quarter of the authorities stated the objective of providing a *resource centre or outreach service*; for example, 'to provide a focal point for resources for community and hospital staff. To provide outreach support and continuing support' (West Lambeth HA geriatric day unit).

Providing basic personal care services was stated as an objective by a small proportion of authorities, as were *support and advice* to individuals, and *teaching and training staff*, which tended to be given as an aim by psychogeriatric day hospitals; for example, 'The unit provides and encourages integrated training and shared work experience between the professional and voluntary agencies' (Grimsby HA day unit).

Where the objectives given for psychogeriatric day hospitals could be distinguished from those for geriatric day hospitals or day hospitals for elderly people in general, some differences emerged. Psychogeriatric day hospitals were more likely than others to state aims of assessment and monitoring, relief for carers, and social care, and less likely to state rehabilitation and treatment.

Differences in objectives between day centres and day hospitals
The responses from SSDs and DHAs reflect the views expressed in several studies that day hospitals' functions are very different from those of day centres. In 1970 Brocklehurst stressed that, 'At the outset it is important to distinguish between day centres and geriatric day hospitals. Day centres provide social facilities—company, a cooked meal, possibly a bath and chiropody, but none of the remedial services found in the day hospital'.[12] Figure 3.1 shows the main differences in objectives between day centres and day hospitals which emerged from the authorities' responses. The largest differences are clearly in the objectives of rehabilitation and treatment and social care.

From a study of day hospitals Martin and Millard concluded that, 'The social and therapeutic activities of many of the day hospitals are . . . incompatible'.[13] They recommended small day treatment units for short-term treatment and separate day clubs for longer-term social and nursing support for very disabled elderly people.

In such discussions about the stated aims of day care services, the differences between day hospitals and day centres are usually emphasised by those involved with day hospitals rather than day centres. This was also the case in the responses to CPA's letter. For example, in defining a day hospital South East Kent HA pointed out that 'it is a hospital and, therefore, its purpose is to give medical treatment in the widest sense of that term',

45

Figure 3.1 Differences in SSD and DHA objectives for day centres and day hospitals

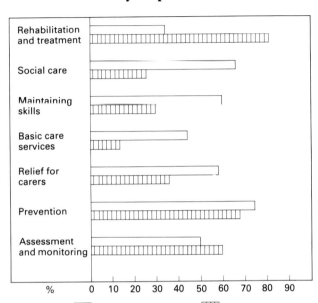

and that 'the day hospital is not a social centre or club for the lonely or housebound elderly. It is the business of the local authority and/or voluntary bodies to provide these facilities'.

It is important, however, to distinguish between types of day hospital. The main objectives of the geriatric day hospital are stated as short-term treatment and rehabilitation. The psychogeriatric day hospital, however, provides longer-term social support for mentally dependent people, in addition to short-term treatment and rehabilitation. According to their stated aims then, there are three main types of day care service: long-term care at day centres in the community or in residential homes; short-term rehabilitation at geriatric day hospitals; and both long- and short-term care at psychogeriatric day hospitals. Another question, however, is the extent to which these stated differences in objectives and function are maintained in practice in the day units.

Types of definitions and objectives

Analysis of the SSD and DHA responses shows that, on the whole, definitions, aims and objectives are neither well distinguished nor clearly stated. The objectives given by these authorities are a combination of the theoretical and the operational and include examples of the functions and components of day services. Clearer distinctions between these dimensions would facilitate various tasks such as the discussion of day care, policy formulation, service planning and management, monitoring and evaluation, and devising programmes for individual users.

Such distinctions are made by some writers. Donaldson and his colleagues, for example, classify the objectives of day hospitals into two strategic ones: 'to facilitate and prolong independent living for the elderly in the community' and 'the promotion of early discharge of elderly in-patients and the prevention of unnecessary admissions'; and four operational ones: 'rehabilitation and maintenance of patients', 'monitoring and review of patients on a regular basis', 'investigation and short-term follow-up of patients', and 'maintenance of contact with those people in the community who care for the patient'.[14]

A number of social services and health authorities defined different types of service or set out a general philosophy then gave specific aims. Barnet SSD, in a review of day care for elderly people, presented a table of five strategic aims, for example 'respite for the carer', with corresponding specific objectives such as 'to provide flexible attendance to meet needs of carer' and 'to contain the person who is mentally infirm in a safe environment'. Such systematic statements of aims are more useful than very brief or vague paragraphs about keeping elderly people in the community and providing hot meals.

We suggest that when developing or reviewing policies for day care services, service providers or individual units clearly formulate their definitions and objectives according to the following categories as appropriate to their purpose.

Types of definitions and objectives

1. Practical, operational definition of the day care services under consideration.
2. Operational definition for each type of service.

3. Statement of the theoretical or strategic objectives of each service.
4. More detailed statement of specific aims related to the theoretical objectives.
5. Statement of how each aim will be met.

REFERENCES
1. Central Council for Education and Training in Social Work, *Day services. An action plan for training*, report of the working party on training for employment in day centres providing care, education and occupation opportunities, CCETSW, London, 1975
2. CCETSW, *Day services*, p 48
3. C. Cantley and G. Smith, Day care for the elderly, in G. Horobin (ed), *Why day care?*, Research highlights in social work 14, Jessica Kingsley, London, 1987, p 29
4. A. Osborn, *Day care for older people in day centres*, Age Concern Scotland, Edinburgh, 1985, p 2
5. J.C. Brocklehurst, *The geriatric day hospital*, King's Fund, London, 1970, p 11
6. J. Carter, *Day services for adults—somewhere to go*, George Allen and Unwin, London, 1981, p 2
7. A. Norton, B. Stoten and H. Taylor, *Councils of care: planning a local government strategy for older people*, Centre for Policy on Ageing, London, 1986, pp 138–40
8. E.M. Goldberg and N. Connelly, *The effectiveness of social care for the elderly*, Policy Studies Institute, London, 1982, p 122
9. Goldberg and Connelly, *The effectiveness of social care*, p 121
10. J.C. Brocklehurst and J.S. Tucker, *Progress in geriatric day care*, King's Fund, London, 1980, p 174
11. Carter, *Day services for adults*
12. Brocklehurst, *The geriatric day hospital*, p 11
13. A. Martin and P.H. Millard, *Day hospitals for the elderly: therapeutic or social?*, St George's Hospital, London, 1978, p 56
14. C. Donaldson, K. Wright and A. Maynard, *Utilisation and performance of day hospitals for the elderly in South Yorkshire*, a report to the Trent Regional Health Authority by the Centre for Health Economics, University of York, 1985, ch 3

4 Current provision of day care services

The escalation of day care services, documented in chapter 1, has resulted in a patchy service, with the level of contribution from the different sectors varying from place to place and rarely based on the assessed needs of the different elderly client groups in an area. In this chapter we examine how much day care is provided, in what ways and for whom. We also consider ways in which needs are assessed, the characteristics of day care users, and the extent to which particular groups of users are offered separate provision. First we look at different ways of categorising the types of day care services which fall within the ambit of our operational definition given in chapter 3.

Types of day care service

The classification of day care services for older people is a difficult task because these services do not fall into tidy categories, and because, as the NISW study showed, day places for older people are provided not only in units for the elderly but also in centres for people who are mentally ill, physically handicapped, or for a combination of groups.[1] Previous studies have classified the services according to four main factors: service provider (health, social services or voluntary); location (day hospital, community-based centre, residential home); whether open most days (full-time) or only one, two or three days (part-time); and whether users are brought in by the service provider's transport.

The NISW study findings suggested that transport provision was a useful way of distinguishing between types of social services and voluntary organisation day centres; it was found that, 'Centres offering transport to their users were smaller, and their users attended for fewer days in any week and also reported much more disability'.[2] Transport could also be the basis for distinction between the two main types of day services noted by Goldberg and Connelly: 'the "senior citizen" centre, offering at best not only a meal but many other social and educational opportunities to ordinary, fairly mobile elderly people'; and 'the day care centre which caters for referred, carefully assessed elderly clients with particular physical or mental disabilities or needs'.[3]

For our purposes of compiling an overall picture of the services provided nationally without undertaking a systematic survey we had to rely on categories in which information might be available from the various sources. This meant using administrative categories such as the service provider and the location of services, while recognising the importance of other, more functional classifications. We have not included day care offered by the private sector in day centres or residential homes, but acknowledge that although this is very limited at present, it is likely to be an expanding source of day care services in the future. The main types of provision considered in this study are thus:

1. *NHS day hospitals for elderly people*, which are classified by health authorities as geriatric or psychogeriatric day hospitals, although geriatric units usually have a proportion of elderly people with mental illness, especially if there is no specialist psychogeriatric unit in the locality.

2. *SSD community-based day centres* for elderly people or for combined client groups. This type now includes an increasing number of specialist units for elderly mentally infirm people.

3. *SSD day care in residential homes for elderly people*, usually offering day places for people who are fairly dependent, physically and/or mentally.

4. *Community-based day centres run by voluntary organisations* for elderly people or mixed client groups, and also including specialist day centres for elderly people with mental disabilities.

The social services or voluntary community-based centres include extended lunch clubs, day clubs or drop-in centres if these are open for at least four hours during the day, offer some form of care and have care givers present. In all four main categories there is a growing number of joint-financed units, especially where provision is made for elderly mentally infirm people for whom collaboration between the sectors is particularly appropriate. As many writers have commented, there is considerable overlap between the services; recent developments such as medical input to day centres, or day hospitals moving into the community, have further blurred the edges of the different types of day care.

Although a certain amount of information on the four types of day care service is available from government and other statistical sources, and most of the health and social services authorities sent statistical data in response to the CPA trawl (see chapter 1), difficulties remain in building up a useful profile of the total level and spread of provision. First, the lack of coterminosity between many health authorities and social services departments is an obstacle to compiling an overall picture of day care provision for the elderly population of a particular area. Second, the data are not collected in any consistent way between the different sectors, and information on voluntary agency services is very sparse especially when these are not supported financially by statutory bodies. Some SSDs include provision by the voluntary sector in their total numbers of day care places, whereas others provide this information separately and the remainder have little or no information on voluntary sector services. Third, statistics giving the number of places available have little meaning when not related to the number of times per week the unit is open and the actual attendance or occupancy levels. Fourth, it is not always possible to distinguish to which client groups a service is offered.

Level and spread of provision
Previous research found the level and spread of day care services to be unsatisfactory. The DHSS studies revealed that services were unevenly distributed within the areas covered, and that distribution was not related to need.[4] Evidence of 'territorial injustice' included lack of provision for the more dependent groups in some areas, lack of suitable services in an individual's own locality, and a varying level of involvement by residential homes in providing day care.[5] These studies also concluded that the level of provision was too low and that there was a demand for its extension so that all areas would have a range of provision.

The NISW study found variations in the 13 sample areas in the type of day centre provision: in three areas almost all day care services were based in residential homes; five relied on the voluntary sector for all types of day centre, while three depended on the SSD; the other two used SSD centres for transport users and voluntary agency centres for other users. There were also wide variations between local authorities in the number of users catered for and the researchers commented that, 'Irrespective of the types of day centres they provide, the local authorities differ dramatically in the amount'.[6] The data collected for the present study suggest that this imbalance has not changed very much, although the total amount of provision has increased since the 1970s.

Table 4.1 Estimated numbers of day care units and places per day* offered to elderly people by four main types of service

	units	places per day*
NHS day hospitals	550	15,010
SSD community-based day centres	700	27,580
SSD day places in residential homes	1,870	11,240
Community-based day centres run by voluntary organisations	1,410	12,200
Total	4,530	66,030

* Average number of places per day over a five day week
Sources: CPA trawl. DHSS statistics and research section 2a
DHSS local authority statistics[7]
CIPFA personal social services statistics[8]

Table 4.1 shows the most accurate estimate we are able to provide from the most recent data available for the total number of units and the total number of places per day offered by the four main types of service. We have estimated an average number of places per day over a five day week to give an idea of relative amounts of provision, since many of the voluntary centres are open only once or twice a week whereas most of the statutory services operate a five day week. The figures should be treated as rough estimates since they are based on a number of sources which themselves often consist of estimates.

Differences in the proportions of units and places provided by the four types of services are illustrated in figures 4.1 and 4.2.

Figure 4.1 Proportion of day units by type of service

Figure 4.2 Proportion of places per day by type of service

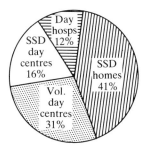

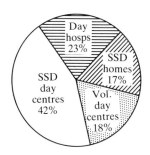

Thus while day hospitals and SSD day centres provide just over a quarter of the units, they offer nearly two-thirds of the available places. On the other hand, whereas elderly people's homes and voluntary day centres account for nearly three-quarters of the units, they provide just over one-third of the places. This is because the number of day places in each home is often very small, and because many voluntary day centres are open less frequently than statutory ones.

Provision of day centres
The figures for estimated total provision do not reflect variations between areas, such as those found by the NISW study which showed that the estimated number of day care places in the 13 sample authorities ranged from 0.8 to 25.8 per 1,000 people aged over 65.[9] The most recent DHSS figures for the number of SSD day centre places for elderly people in the population of the nine regions of England ranged from 0.7 per 1,000 over 65s in the south western region to 8.0 in London, with an average of 3.0. Within these regional totals the rate ranged from 0.3 to 41.7 with a median of 3.2 places per 1,000 over 65s. The lowest rates tended to be for non-metropolitan counties whereas the highest were for London boroughs. To some extent this reflects a tendency of county authorities to rely more on the voluntary sector for day care services.

53

The level of take-up of available places also varies considerably. The NISW study found an average occupancy rate of 70%.[10] Occupancy rates for SSD day centres cited by a few respondents to the CPA trawl suggest a mismatch between needs and resources in some areas; the rates ranged from 30% to 176% with a median of 81%. Thus both underuse and over-occupancy were reported, making it difficult to generalise about the extent to which resources met needs. A more accurate picture of use of day care resources is provided by attendance figures since the number of places seems to be rather notional.

Table 4.2 Estimated numbers of client days in SSD day care units per 1,000 over 65s for the year 1987–88 in England and Wales

	Non-metropolitan counties	Metropolitan districts	London boroughs
Day centres			
lowest	16	29	138
highest	1,284	4,105	5,286
median	342	680	657
average	284	591	1,240
Residential centres			
lowest	9	19	22
highest	583	746	566
median	156	241	116
average	134	192	63
Total day centres and residential centres			
lowest	236	52	254
highest	1,418	4,125	5,336
median	600	840	1,002
average	418	783	1,303

Source: CIPFA personal social services statistics[11]

Analysis of CIPFA estimates for the number of client days during 1987–88 in SSD day centres and residential centres, and of population figures for people aged over 65 produced the results shown in table 4.2. This illustrates, again, the wide disparity in levels of provision between areas, and shows that the lowest levels are for the counties, then the metropolitan districts, and that the highest levels are for London boroughs.

The large differences in total levels confirm that authorities with low provision of one type of service do not necessarily compensate for this by a higher level of another service. The data collected for this study on voluntary organisation services suggest that there is no reason to suppose that services are more evenly distributed in the voluntary sector.

Provision of day hospitals
It seemed likely that geriatric day hospitals would be more evenly spread than day centres, with one or more in almost all health districts, although these may be at some distance from users in parts of the district. For example, a recent study of the South West Thames region found that there were 26 geriatric day hospitals, at least one in each of the 13 health districts.[12] This survey did not include psychogeriatric day hospitals which are probably less evenly distributed. The MIND study sample found an average of 1.0 psychogeriatric day hospital places per 1,000 over 65s, with rates ranging from 0.4 to 1.5 per 1,000.[13]

The data sent in response to the CPA letter allowed, in some cases, for the calculation of numbers of places per 1,000 over 65s. This showed a median of 1.8 geriatric day hospital places and 1.3 places in psychogeriatric day hospitals per 1,000 people over 65. As for day centres, however, the number of day hospital places officially designated did not reflect the actual attendances since places were under- or over-occupied. Attendance figures supplied by the DHSS for the 14 regions of England were used to calculate attendance rates per 1,000 over 65s. These ranged from 140 attendances per year in North West Thames region to 481 in North Western region with a median of 330.

Another measure of variation between day hospitals which affects the level of places available is the ratio of new patients to total attendances during the year. Martin and Millard[14] devised the corrected new patient index (CPNI) with the simple formula:

$$\frac{\text{number of new patients in the year} \times 10}{\text{total number of attendances in year}}$$

A ratio near to 0 indicates a more custodial day hospital, whereas the nearer to 1, the more rehabilitative is the hospital. For a small number of districts or hospitals we were able to calculate the CPNI from data returned to CPA. The index ranged from 0.13 to 1.09 for geriatric day hospitals with a median of 0.47. For psychogeriatric day hospitals the CPNI was, as expected, lower, ranging from 0.04 to 0.58 with a median of 0.21. These figures are intended to be illustrative rather than representative.

In summary, then, the overall picture is of an uneven level and spread of provision of all types of day care, both within and between the types of service. We should emphasise that this profile is not a static one. The impression conveyed by those of our respondents who gave details of new units or places planned is that day care services will continue to expand and that they will also develop in some innovative ways which we shall describe in chapter 7.

Assessment of needs for day care services
As the evidence above has shown, in some areas a mismatch between needs and provision indicates that local needs have not been assessed, nor has provision been planned for the area. This is not surprising in the context of competing priorities and decreasing resources. Some authorities, however, compared their own provision with national norms, and a few undertook surveys which revealed the extent of unmet need. For example, in one area a questionnaire on day services identified over 300 individual elderly people whose needs for day care were not being met. On the other hand, several authorities mentioned that attendance at day hospitals was well below the available capacity. Assessment of need, then, was mainly on an individual basis.

Referral and assessment of need for day care has tended to be limited to a particular service or unit, as individuals are assessed not for the most appropriate form of care but for the service to which they are referred. A study of day care services in Medway found that professionals usually referred to the same services, for example consultants to the day hospital or social workers to the day centre so that 'particular day services could almost be seen as "belonging" to particular professions'.[15] Further, several writers have pointed out that the various day care services are not always considered in the wider context of the other community care services which could help meet the assessed needs of older individuals and their carers. There are, however, exceptions; for example, Newcastle SSD states in 'Proposals for future development' that 'persons will be admitted to day centres only after a problem-based assessment which leads to care packaging in which a day centre is a key element'.

According to recent studies, respondents to CPA's letter and seminar participants, systems of referral, admission criteria and assessment procedures vary between types of provision and service providers.

Referral and assessment for day centres
A common feature of voluntary day centres and of some SSD centres is that access for fit and mobile elderly people is fairly open, with little referral or assessment. But Tibbitt points out that in consequence 'users are to a significant extent a self-selected group who may not always comprise those who might benefit most from the day facilities available'.[16] Other SSD centres and residential home day places are strictly limited to those most in need. Specialist centres for elderly mentally infirm people, whether organised by the SSD or voluntary agencies, usually have formal criteria and procedures. For example, Alison Norman quotes the admission criteria for a specialist voluntary day centre: 'Clients must have characteristics, whether of personality disorder, functional illness or confusion, which make them unacceptable in ordinary day centres'.[17]

The criteria for acceptance into SSD day care services, cited by respondents to the CPA letter, embraced a wide span of characteristics and reflected the many facets of older people's circumstances. Two-fifths of the 60 criteria mentioned could be classified as *physical handicap*, which included frailty, physical or sensory disability, impaired mobility, wheelchair use, and being housebound; being elderly was also cited, as was a lower age limit of 60 with exceptions for younger people in special cases. The next most frequent category (23%) comprised *physical needs* such as incontinence, help with self-care, nutrition, hygiene, and remedial therapy. *Mental disabilities* accounted for 13% of the criteria and included mild confusion or dementia, mental illness or occasional aggression. *Social needs* related to loneliness, isolation, grief, depression and withdrawal comprised 12% of the criteria. A further 12% concerned the *individual's circumstances*, such as needs for counselling and advice, moving to residential care, preventing admission to hospital, and enabling carers to go to work or have a break.

Criteria for refusal almost all concerned two of these categories and were equally divided between them. The most demanding physical needs, particularly incontinence and needs for nursing or medical care, and the more serious mental disabilities such as severe dementia, wandering, behaviour problems and personality disorders, were the most frequently cited barriers to SSD day care admission. Similar conditions, however, were given as criteria for acceptance into specialist units. For example, a centre for mentally infirm elderly people accepted those with mental disabilities, such as dementia and confusion, lacking orientation and being a danger to themselves and to others, and with physical needs including help with incontinence, self-care and health care. Referrals for SSD day care were usually made by professionals to the SSD area office for assessment by social workers following a set procedure. This typically included consultation with other health and welfare professionals, day care managers and with the elderly person and any carers. A form was completed, then a decision taken by the responsible person, for example a senior social worker or day centre manager, or by a panel of social work, day unit and other staff. If there was a waiting list, assessment would inevitably be used as a rationing device; examples were given of priority categories, with elderly people at risk in the home, or carers under extreme stress receiving top priority. A Dorset County Council study group on day care commented that the criteria were severe but that 'any reduction in the severity of the criteria would result in places in the centre going to clients with fewer needs and, therefore, with a lower priority', and urged that alternatives be considered so that 'scarce day centre places should be restricted to clients who cannot be looked after in their own homes or in the voluntary sector'.

Referral and assessment for day hospitals
Day hospitals apparently had less need for rationing devices, and assessment often followed rather than preceded admission

to the unit. Criteria for referral to a geriatric day hospital were less diverse than those for SSD day care. *Physical needs* comprised one-half of the criteria mentioned by respondents to CPA's letter and included needs for clinical assessment and treatment, rehabilitation, therapy and nursing. Over one-third of the criteria concerned the *individual's circumstances*, such as need for support to prevent admission to hospital or while awaiting Part III accommodation, preparation for discharge from hospital or need for care, treatment and rehabilitation after discharge. *Social needs* formed a very small category, stressed as exceptional, and the only other criterion mentioned was age, over 65. Criteria for refusal of admission to a geriatric day hospital included the *mental disabilities* such as dementia or psychiatric problems which were criteria for admission to psychogeriatric day hospitals. Some day hospitals also rejected people who were aged under 65 or had social needs only.

The sources of referral to day hospitals were predominantly medical. Almost three-quarters of referral sources mentioned were doctors, equally divided between GPs and hospital doctors. Other sources were remedial therapists, social workers, community psychiatric nurses (CPNs), and Age Concern. Most referrals followed an out-patient clinic attendance, a domiciliary visit by a consultant, or discharge from an in-patient ward, or were made from an in-patient or assessment ward. Only exceptionally would referral result from a home visit by a GP, CPN or social worker.

Almost invariably referrals were made to the consultant geriatrician or psychogeriatrician at the day hospital. The typical procedure was for the elderly person to be seen by the consultant or senior medical member of the multi-disciplinary team. Then the patient would be assessed by each member of the team at initial attendances at the day hospital, or occasionally at home or in the out-patients department. The elderly person's attendance programme would subsequently be decided at a multi-disciplinary meeting. The purpose of initial assessment at a day hospital is thus not so much to decide whether or not people will be admitted, as to determine the number of days per week they will attend, and their treatment and rehabilitation programme. This assessment is an integral part of the service, whether the aim is short-term attendance at a geriatric day hospital or longer-term support in a psychogeriatric day hospital.

The users of day care services

From recent surveys and the information sent in response to the CPA letter we can illustrate the demographic and other characteristics of day care users, although the figures are not claimed to be representative. The proportion of women was higher among day care users than in the elderly population and higher in day centres than in day hospitals. In Medway health district 71% of day care attenders were women, compared with 60% of the over 65 population.[18] Recent surveys showed that in day hospitals in Worcester and Chichester 62% and 63% of patients were women; in day centres in South Glamorgan and Barnet, however, 73% and 76% of users were women. These differences were partly due to the ages of users, as day centre users tended to be older and the ratio of women to men increases with age. For example in South Glamorgan 69% of users under 70 were women, compared with 72% of those in their seventies and 77% in their eighties.

The Medway study found that 70% of users were over 75, compared with 40% of the over 65 population.[19] In South West Thames region 70% of geriatric day hospital patients were over 75 with a mean age of 78.8 and ages ranging from 54 to 98, an age structure which was 'similar though slightly older than that reported in previous day hospital surveys'.[20] That survey, however, did not include psychogeriatric day hospitals where patients tend to be younger. The South Glamorgan and Barnet surveys found that 82% and 85% respectively of day centre users were over 70; 47% and 41% were in their seventies and 34% and 44% were over 80. There was little information about ages of voluntary day centre users but these seemed to be mainly in their seventies and eighties.

Two-fifths of day service attenders lived alone, according to the Medway survey.[21] People attending day hospitals were less likely to live alone than those attending day centres and those attending units for elderly mentally infirm people were much less likely to live alone. One-third of South West Thames day hospital attenders lived alone; in South Glamorgan, however, 64% of day centre clients lived alone, 17% lived with a spouse, 15% with relatives and 4% in other types of household.

Physical disabilities and chronic illnesses were common in all types of day care unit, including voluntary day centres. Arthritis and impaired mobility were the most usual physical problems of day centre users. In Barnet SSD day centres 36% of users had physical disabilities and another 13% had psychiatric and physical disabilities; in Tower Hamlets two-thirds were physically disabled. The most frequent physical problem of day hospital patients was cerebrovascular disease (including strokes), suffered by 32% of patients in South West Thames and 36% in Chichester. This was followed by musculoskeletal diseases (including arthritis) in 30% of South West Thames patients and 29% in Chichester. The South West Thames study commented that patients' diagnoses were similar to those of previous studies except that the proportion with musculoskeletal diseases had doubled.[22]

Physical dependence was consequently reported in all types of units, with the highest levels in day hospitals. In Medway day units 41% of attenders used a walking frame or wheelchair but the proportion was 60% in the day hospital and 63% in the joint-financed unit. Among Barnet day centre members 9% used a wheelchair whereas a Worcester day hospital reported 75% wheelchair use. The South West Thames survey found that 84% of geriatric day hospital patients were dependent in needing help from another person to perform any of the activities assessed.[23] The over 85s and stroke patients had the highest levels of dependence. About one-half of day care centre users were neither physically nor mentally dependent. A dependence questionnaire completed for day care centre users in Gwynedd showed that 52% were not dependent; 21% were alert but had limited physical ability; 9% had high physical ability but were occasionally confused; 9% had limited physical ability and were occasionally confused; and another 9% were very dependent physically and/or mentally.

Examples given of the proportion of day unit attenders with dementia or confusion varied between types of unit. The Medway study found that, overall, 73% of users were almost never confused, 19% were sometimes and 8% almost always confused, with the highest levels of confusion, as expected, in the units specialising in mental infirmity, one of which had 63% of users with confusion.[24] The incidence of dementia or confusion was low in geriatric day hospitals, for example 7% in South West Thames region where there were psychogeriatric day hospitals in all districts except one.[25] A substantial proportion of day centre users had dementia, for example one-third of attenders in SSD day centres in Tower Hamlets and 15% in Barnet. The Barnet day centres had 12% of users with psychiatric illnesses and another 13% with psychiatric and physical disabilities. A survey of voluntary day centres in Croydon showed that all the centres had one or two members with confusion or psychiatric problems and that two centres had a higher number of confused attenders, at least two per day. The Medway study showed that 40% of users of all types of day centres were sometimes depressed and 5% almost always depressed; thus depression was more widespread among day service users than dementia, as earlier studies had shown.[26] The incidence of dementia in day centres, however, seemed to be increasing.

At least four-fifths of day care users attended for one or two days a week. The Medway survey found that 57% of users attended once a week and 32% twice a week, with the highest level of attendance, 59% for three or more times a week, at a unit for elderly mentally ill people.[27] In Barnet SSD day centres 44% attended once a week and 38% twice a week, while in Liverpool 75% attended twice a week. At a Worcester day hospital, 80% of patients attended twice a week and 15% once a week. Whereas day centre users had often been attending for two years or more, length of attendance at day hospitals was measured in weeks; for example at a Chichester day hospital 41% had attended for less than 4 weeks, 32% from 4 to 8 weeks, 24% from 8 to 16 weeks and 4% for more than 16 weeks.

The more dependent users of day care services were likely also to be receiving other support services. A study by Cambridgeshire SSD found that three-fifths of day centre attenders received such services: 47% had home helps, 20% meals on wheels and 30% a community nurse.[28] Comparing day centre users with residents of old people's homes the researchers found the two groups very similar in levels of dependence and incidence of confusion and disability, although the residents were older. A review of home help clients attending day care in Coventry examined the characteristics and services received by the 4.2% of all home help clients who attended SSD day care and the 1.6% attending day hospital. Day hospital attenders were found to be younger and less likely to live alone than SSD day care users or home help clients as a whole. The proportion of SSD day care users who had a social worker (47%) was very much higher than for all home help clients (18%) or for day hospital patients (34%). Day hospital attenders, however, were more likely to have a community nurse (59%) than home help clients as a whole (33%) or SSD day care attenders. These findings suggest that people already receiving social work and community nursing services as well as home help are most likely to be referred for day care. Others not known to the domiciliary services and who do not know about day care may have similar needs which are unmet.

Some respondents to the CPA letter commented about groups which did not receive day care services; for example, Dudley SSD day centres did not cater for aggressive or severely confused people and Frenchay HA had no day hospital provision for elderly mentally infirm people. A paper from Lewisham SSD pointed out that the open door policy had meant that the more fit and mobile elderly people, mainly white women, used the centres whereas those with special or different needs were not catered for. Studies have shown that previous attenders who had left day units for a variety of reasons including illness, mobility problems and criticisms of the service provided, still had the same needs which were now unmet.[29,30]

As mentioned earlier, a mismatch was found between needs and provision, which confirmed the findings of studies in the 1970s.[31,32,33] More recent surveys have shown little change in this phenomenon as far as users are concerned. For example, in Medway 'substantial numbers of patients did not seem to "fit" the service which they were attending'.[34] A joint working party on day care in Coventry found that when users in five types of day care unit were assessed according to four dependence ratings, the researchers considered that about one-third of users could have managed in a different type of unit. The South West Thames survey found no consistent relationship between patients' dependence levels and the levels of remedial therapy staff in different day hospitals.[35] Day centres run by voluntary organisations were sometimes having to cope with a higher level of dependence among users than they could manage, as Osborn pointed out.[36]

It seems, then, that although on the whole day hospital users are both younger and more dependent than users of other day care services, there is considerable overlap between the characteristics of users of the different types of service, and little clear relationship between dependence levels and the services provided. Further, there are people receiving little or no day care who are more dependent or have more specialised needs than those who most frequently use day care services. Elderly people who are mentally infirm, incontinent, psychiatrically disturbed, very disabled, or from ethnic minorities are among those whose needs are not fully met.

Provision for special groups: integrated or separate?
There is an increasing trend, revealed by DHSS statistics, for local authorities to provide day centres for mixed groups of clients.[37] Whether or not this is beneficial for clients is a matter of debate. Jan Carter pointed out that the main motivation underlying this trend is to make the most efficient use of the building.[38] The NISW study found that only 2% of units were mixed, most of them run by SSDs for a combination of handicaps and age groups. There were two main ways of mixing: different groups using separate parts of the building or associating freely together. Carter noted that although heads of units were satisfied with the free association model, staff and users were not so enthusiastic.

Studies have shown that mixing older and younger physically handicapped people or physically and mentally handicapped people of different age groups, often worked successfully. For example, a study of a day centre for both mobile and handicapped elderly people found 'no underlying strain or evidence of ill-feeling or friction between younger and older clients, the more and less able, referred or drop-in clients or between any other groups'.[39] At a combined day centre for physically handicapped, mentally handicapped and mentally ill people the groups shared activities and helped each other.[40] But some writers expressed caution about mixed day centres and reported negative attitudes of elderly people to mixing with other groups. Dorset SSD's elderly day care study group considered it inappropriate to integrate elderly users with other groups and advocated multi-purpose centres with separable sections and toilet facilities, and the use of centres or parts of a centre by different groups at different times.

Even where day centres are not officially mixed, there are often a few people from different groups among the users. Many writers have commented that elderly confused people were the group least welcomed by others and there is now fairly widespread support for separate day care facilities for elderly people who are mentally infirm. The East Anglia study recommended this in the interests both of the mentally infirm users and of efficient use of centres since 'the cost of integrating the confused is the loss of more typical day centre users'.[41]

Respondents to the CPA letter cited many examples of specialist units provided or planned, including joint-financed or voluntary agency units. For example, in Greenwich, Age Concern and MIND run a day centre twice a week for elderly confused people. Buckinghamshire SSD prefers to integrate people except when this is inappropriate; in the county there are small, specialist day care schemes and day care for elderly mentally infirm people in some of the authority's residential homes, and a new specialist facility is planned for people with advanced dementia. Other day centres or hospitals offer separate facilities or days for elderly mentally infirm people. In Maidstone, for instance, a new day hospital will have shared activity room, kitchen, toilets and transport, but other accommodation will be separate for elderly physically frail and mentally infirm people.

The East Anglia study also recommended separate units for elderly people with psychiatric disorders.[42] Alison Norman pointed out the difficulties of mixing mentally infirm with mentally ill people in psychogeriatric day hospitals.[43] But few examples of separate provision for people with functional mental illness were offered by our respondents.

Another question is whether day care in residential homes should use separate facilities or be integrated within the home. Evidence from the NISW project suggested that 'the "segregated" pattern is to be preferred, since it deals with clashes over the priority accorded to residents and day care users which tend to be acute in the "integrated centres" '.[44] A CPA study of residential homes, some of which attempted to integrate day users while others made separate provision, stressed the importance of adequate space and staffing and careful planning including consideration of people's feelings about the use of private space.[45]

In policy documents sent in response to CPA's trawl there was little discussion of these difficult issues. Some local authorities rely on Part III homes for SSD-provided day care. Wiltshire SSD provides its 'primary' day care (for more dependent older people) on the integrated model in old people's homes and supports voluntary organisations in the provision of 'secondary' day care in community-based day centres. In a paper for Waltham Forest social services committee, however, officers recommended phasing out day care in Part III homes, because of growing pressures for residential places, because residents, staff and day care attenders were adversely affected by the service, and because providing day care in residential homes was not an efficient use of resources.

In day hospitals the question of integrating in-patients and day attenders is less difficult because the day hospital is normally separate from in-patient wards and thus does not intrude on in-patients' private space. Integration of equal numbers of in-patients and day patients was considered beneficial for example in Farnham, where in-patients mixed with patients from the community at the day hospital which they continued to attend after discharge. Similarly, where a separate day unit is provided in a residential home, residents and non-residents can mix together, returning to their own home or private space at the end of the day. Residents of homes also sometimes continue to attend community-based day centres after moving into the home.

Although day care services are open to elderly people from any background, there is now a considerable body of opinion in favour of specialist units for people from ethnic minorities. Alison Norman identified negative and positive reasons for this; for example, ethnic minority elders were not welcomed by day centre members, the food was not appropriate, and there were language and cultural barriers; but there were also needs to relax and socialise with people from the same background, to learn skills, read newspapers and watch videos about people's own culture.[46] Day centres for ethnic minorities are also important sources of information and advice, and often operate on a self-help basis.

Some respondents to CPA's letter were concerned about low uptake of day centre places by people from ethnic minorities, but also recognised that special dietary, religious, cultural and language needs were not met by such day centres. The local authorities' response was not usually specialist SSD provision but to grant-aid ethnic minority organisations to run their own day centres. Such voluntary centres were however often very under-resourced in comparison with SSD centres.

Information on specialist day centres from our respondents and other sources shows that the main groups catered for are Afro-Caribbean and Asian people, and that the provision is, as expected, mainly in London boroughs and metropolitan districts, for example Enfield, Lewisham, Leicester and Wolverhampton. Some non-metropolitan counties also gave examples. Berkshire SSD mentioned voluntary day centres for West Indian women and for Muslim women, and Lancashire SSD cited two day centres for Asian people and one for West Indians. There were also well-established Jewish day centres such as those in Enfield and Harrow, and centres for elderly Cypriots in Enfield and Haringey. More recently day centres for Vietnamese and Chinese people have been set up, for example in Lewisham and Greenwich, and Liverpool SSD devoted one day a week at a day centre to Chinese elderly people.

At a conference on day care organised in November 1987 by the Standing Committee for Ethnic Minority Senior Citizens (SCEMSC) it was acknowledged that it was difficult to get elderly people to change, that the long-term aim of integrating ethnic minority elderly people into ordinary day centres should be approached gradually, and that staff training was essential. Participants suggested that if a separate centre was not available, ethnic minority groups could at first use an existing day centre on separate days, then eventually the groups might work together. It was felt that local authorities should reallocate day care resources so that services for ethnic minorities received a fair share. The Director of SCEMSC recently called for mainstream funding for services for ethnic minority elders and a code of practice for voluntary day centres.[47]

Information needs on current provision of day care services
This review of the level, spread and type of day care services currently provided has relied on statistics, estimates and examples from various readily available sources. It has revealed a lack of accurate, updated, accessible and consistent data,

which must constitute a barrier to careful planning of day care services at national or local levels. Many authorities are now trying to remedy this by setting up joint working parties to review all day care services in the area. The monitoring of day care services at local and national levels is considered further in chapter 8.

We suggest that authorities collate the following information for use in monitoring day care services.

Basic items of information
1. Definition of the types of day care unit under consideration and the client groups to be catered for in each.

2. Identification of local needs for such provision for different groups of the elderly population, including those with special needs.

3. Comparison of identified needs with current provision.

4. Basic data on the services provided or planned, including the number and location of units, the days open, the number of places per week in each, and attendance figures.

5. Information on the role of each unit, the groups catered for (or excluded), referral and admission criteria and procedures, and transport arrangements, widely available to the different professionals and agencies in the area, as well as to elderly people and carers.

More detailed information would include the various components of the day care services to which we turn in chapter 5.

REFERENCES
1. J. Carter, *Day services for adults—somewhere to go*, George Allen and Unwin, London, 1981
2. C. Edwards, I. Sinclair and P. Gorbach, Day centres for the elderly: variations in the type, provision and user response, *British Journal of Social Work*, 10, 1980, 419–30
3. E.M. Goldberg and N. Connelly, *The effectiveness of social care for the elderly*, Policy Studies Institute, London, 1982, pp 131–32
4. G. Fennell, A.R. Emerson, M. Sidell and A. Hague, *Day centres for the elderly in East Anglia*, University of East Anglia School of Economic and Social Studies, Norwich, 1981

5. R. Bowl, H. Taylor, M. Taylor and N. Thomas, *Day care for the elderly in Birmingham*, University of Birmingham Social Services Unit, Birmingham, 1978

6. Edwards *et al*, Day centres for the elderly, p 423

7. Department of Health and Social Security, *Adult training centres for mentally handicapped people and day centres for mentally ill, elderly and younger physically handicapped people at 31 March 1986, England*, government statistical service, London, 1986

8. The Chartered Institute of Public Finance and Accountancy, *Personal social services statistics 1987-88 estimates*, CIPFA, London, 1987

9. Carter, *Day services for adults*

10. Carter, *Day services for adults*

11. CIPFA, *Personal social services statistics*

12. E. Haworth, *A survey of geriatric day hospitals in South West Thames regional health authority*, South West Thames RHA, 1987

13. S.M. Peace, *Caring from day to day*, MIND, London, 1980

14. A. Martin and P.H. Millard, *Day hospitals for the elderly: therapeutic or social?*, St George's Hospital, London, 1978, p 27

15. J. Pahl, *Day services for elderly people in Medway health district*, Health services research unit, University of Kent, Canterbury, 1986, p 28

16. J.E. Tibbitt, Day care—a 'good thing'? in G. Horobin (ed), *Why day care?*, Research highlights in social work 14, Jessica Kingsley, London, 1987, p 21

17. A. Norman, *Mental illness in old age: meeting the challenge*, Centre for Policy on Ageing, London, 1982, p 81

18. Pahl, *Day services in Medway*

19. Pahl, *Day services in Medway*

20. Haworth, *Geriatric day hospitals*, p 13

21. Pahl, *Day services in Medway*

22. Haworth, *Geriatric day hospitals*

23. Haworth, *Geriatric day hospitals*

24. Pahl, *Day services in Medway*

25. Haworth, *Geriatric day hospitals*

26. Pahl, *Day services in Medway*

27. Pahl, *Day services in Medway*

28. G. Tuffnell and R.W. Warburton, Elderly users of day care: a census of old people attending Grade 'A' day centres in Cambridgeshire, *Clearing House for Local Authority Social Services Research*, 6, 1981, 27–36

29. Fennell *et al*, *Day centres for the elderly*

30. J. Bligh, Clients' views of day centres for the elderly and physically handicapped in Hammersmith, *Clearing House for Local Authority Social Services Research*, 1, 1979, 1–50

31. Bowl *et al*, *Day care for the elderly*

32. Fennell *et al*, *Day centres for the elderly*

33. J.C. Brocklehurst and J.S. Tucker, *Progress in geriatric day care*, King's Fund, London, 1980

34. Pahl, *Day services in Medway*, p 27

35. Haworth, *Geriatric day hospitals*

36. A. Osborn, *Day care for older people in day centres*, Age Concern Scotland, Edinburgh, 1985

37. DHSS, *Adult training centres and day centres*

38. J. Carter, Mixing up day services, *Community Care*, 418, July 1982

39. P. Fletcher and J. Robinson, *Desborough Hall: study of a day centre*, Buckinghamshire County Council SSD, 1974, p 32

40. C.A. Reed, *Integration of handicaps at a combined day centre*, Leicestershire County Council SSD, 1979

41. Fennell *et al*, *Day centres for the elderly*, p 209

42. Fennell *et al*, *Day centres for the elderly*

43. Norman, *Mental illness in old age*

44. C. Edwards and I. Sinclair, Debate: segregation vs. integration, *Social Work Today*, 11, 40, 1980, 21

45. A. Norman, *Bricks and mortals: design and lifestyle in old people's homes*, Centre for Policy on Ageing, London, 1984

46. A. Norman, *Triple jeopardy: growing old in a second homeland*, Centre for Policy on Ageing, London, 1985

47. S. Daniel, A code to care for elders, *Social Work Today*, 19, 50, 1988, 9

5 Key components of day care services

How, then, are individual day care units organised and how do users spend the time there? In response to CPA's request, nearly one-half of HAs and over two-fifths of SSDs sent information about aspects such as management, premises, activities, staffing and training, funding and costs. We also collected examples at seminars and by visiting units, some of which are described in the case studies below.

Management and control of day care units

Operational policies and other documents produced by the statutory sector often located day unit staff within the authority's management structure. Thus, for example, through line management, day hospital staff were responsible to one of the HA's unit general managers, and day centre staff to an assistant director of the SSD. In the voluntary sector individual day centres were more likely to have their own management committees, as were units run jointly by HAs and SSDs or by statutory and voluntary agencies.

In most day hospitals a nursing sister or charge nurse was responsible for the daily administration of the unit. More rarely an administrator held this responsibility. Consultants, or occasionally a nursing sister or the whole multi-disciplinary team, had clinical charge of the day hospital. Individuals were professionally responsible through their own professional hierarchies. Within the unit senior professionals organised relevant programmes and supervised juniors and assistants. The multi-disciplinary team decided jointly on individual care programmes. A few examples cited key workers from the teams being identified for each patient.

Responsibility for the daily running of SSD or joint-financed day units was usually held by the day centre manager or organiser. In local authority residential homes, however, the officer-in-charge was responsible for the day care places. Some voluntary day centres, especially those receiving statutory funding, had paid organisers, whereas others were run entirely by volunteers. Where there was professional input to SSD or voluntary day centres, workers were professionally accountable through their own structures. In a few day centres a key worker system was used.

Most day hospital operational policies stressed the importance of the multi-disciplinary team. Inter-disciplinary communication was fostered by a structure of regular meetings. Weekly case conferences or review meetings were attended by representatives of all the professions in the day hospital, community and SSD staff, and sometimes by representatives of voluntary organisations. In addition staff often met each morning or afternoon to discuss cases. Some day hospitals had more general multi-disciplinary meetings, for example a three monthly meeting at one day hospital to discuss policy implementation, administrative problems and future development.

Formal communication systems were less frequently mentioned in the data on SSD day centres, although some authorities gave details of regular staff meetings in individual centres. Earlier studies found day centre staff to be professionally isolated.[1] A few authorities such as Gwynedd and Barnet had addressed this problem by arranging regular meetings for managers of several day centres in an area. We shall return to this issue when considering training for day centre staff.

The information sent by SSDs suggested that, as the NISW study showed, centralised management structures for day care were bureaucratic and offered little understanding of the practicalities of day care.[2] There was little control of their own units by local area office or day centre staff, although this happened in a few innovative areas such as Humberside.

The East Anglia study commented on lack of involvement by SSD management in the running and monitoring of day units supported by the department directly or through grant aid.[3] A more recent study of the effects of grant aid to voluntary organisations providing day centres and other welfare services found little accountability to the grant giver.[4] The researchers described such accountability as 'symbolic' consisting mainly of submitting annual reports and accounts, and representation of the grant giving authority on the voluntary organisation's management committee. Our data show that in some areas, for example Norfolk and Wiltshire, SSD managers, having reviewed day care provision, are now actively developing the services and visiting statutory and voluntary day units to promote day care policies and offer guidance.

In the information from our statutory sources accountability through management or professional structures featured more often than accountability to, or involvement of, the day service users. Day patients' participation was usually limited to being consulted about their own care programmes and being involved in the implementation of the multi-disciplinary team's decisions. Social services authorities, where they described the rights of SSD and voluntary day centre users, generally had more active participation in mind. Examples included representation on members' committees; encouragement to express opinions and take part in decision making; arranging outings; helping with domestic tasks; and respect for privacy, dignity and risk taking. The rights of non-users were not addressed in such documents.

Although user participation is not always appropriate for very dependent elderly people and can have negative effects, most writers have advocated greater participation by users. There is evidence that it is possible for members to be very actively involved in running their own centres as, for example in Stockport, or in the centre studied by Hazan.[5,6] But from the information available this seems to be the exception rather than the rule, and participation often remains tokenistic.

The involvement of users' relatives in the day unit and the provision of support for carers are likely to be appropriate where day services cater for more dependent elderly people. Such aspects were mentioned by our informants more frequently in connection with day hospitals than day centres. Operational policies for day hospitals often included carers' participation in decisions affecting the patient or mentioned that relatives were welcome at the unit. In addition to offering individual advice, several day hospitals organised monthly support groups for carers. Examples of similar attention to carers' needs were given by a few SSDs, for example Bedfordshire and Lincolnshire. Very few authorities included information on complaints procedures in their operational policies or other day care documents.

Premises

Although the production of design briefs does not fall within the ambit of the present study, we recognise the need for such specialised guidance, as there is little literature generally available on designing day care units to help people who are planning new centres. A recent report on day care buildings described 19 day units for elderly people; on the basis of these case studies the report considered issues such as client groups, service provision, transport, staffing and activities in relation to design, and gave detailed design considerations for different types of day unit.[7]

A few authorities sent us design documents which considered in detail access, use of space, safety features, decor and environment. Without a systematic survey we could not assess the extent to which premises were suitable. Day care premises included purpose-built or adapted day centres, day hospitals or residential homes; sheltered housing units run by LAs or housing associations; church halls or community centres used for other purposes; and mobile units towed to different locations. The most pertinent issue is the suitability of premises for disabled people, particularly external access at the main entrance, absence of steps within the building, circulation space and toilet facilities.

The adequate provision of space for frequent movement between activities, and flexibility in the use of space were stressed in design documents. Such flexibility not only facilitated the organisation of a range of activities for one group of users, but also allowed premises to be used concurrently or on different days by different client groups. Subdividing large spaces to create a more homely atmosphere, using simple strong furniture, use of colour variations, and views of gardens or street scenes were also advocated as contributing to a pleasant environment for users.

Ideally all premises used for day care should be purpose-built or adapted and equipped for wheelchair users who would otherwise effectively be excluded. But purpose-built or adapted buildings are more likely to be found in the statutory sector, since they may be too expensive for voluntary organisations. The suitability of premises also has to be balanced against the need for localised day care which avoids lengthy journeys and other transport problems.

From the examples received, it seems that at least 50% of day hospitals were purpose-built while the others were adapted, for instance from a ward, or a villa in hospital grounds. Most were situated within or attached to an existing hospital, on the ground floor, with their own entrance or access via the hospital, and had exclusive use of their facilities.

Day care units within the catchment area of an SSD typically included a few purpose-built or adapted centres run directly by the SSD, and a larger number of community-based units run by voluntary organisations, some of which used local authority premises. Purpose-built units were sometimes attached to or close to homes for elderly people or sheltered housing. Although many SSD day care buildings were owned by the SSD, others were rented from health authorities or district councils, or were designated for SSD use in the day time, for example in community schools.

Some voluntary day centres were also situated in or attached to local authority homes or sheltered housing. More generally, however, they used community centres or church halls, or owned or rented, sometimes at a peppercorn rent, their premises. For example, of ten day centres in Croydon, three owned their premises, five rented them, one had free use of council premises and one used church-owned premises.

The actual accommodation, which varied according to the size and needs of the unit, consisted minimally of a large room, kitchen or servery, and toilets. The East Anglia study recommended as minimal requirements for a full-time day centre: a sitting area and dining area with special WCs within easy reach, an office/staff room, storage space, bathroom/laundry room and kitchen.[8] Day hospitals also require treatment rooms and facilities for chiropody, speech therapy and the assessment of daily living skills.

From the examples collected for this study, reception areas seemed of greater importance in day hospitals than other units. A separate reception area was considered desirable, with a receptionist's office, sitting area, cloakroom, toilets and wheelchair park. For units receiving transport users, a loading bay for ambulances was necessary, and a covered canopy, automatic entrance doors and a lobby were often recommended.

Basic activity areas in all types of unit comprised sitting and dining facilities and provision for recreational and therapeutic activities. Less frequently there were additional large or small rooms for separate activities. Adjacent to the dining area there was usually a kitchen for preparing meals or snacks, or a servery for ready-prepared meals.

Most day hospitals had treatment rooms or cubicles where nursing and medical procedures were carried out; medical consultation and examination rooms; and a kitchen, bathroom, and bedroom or complete suite for the assessment of daily living skills. Many also had interview rooms for nurses, therapists and social workers; hairdressing rooms; separate areas for occupational therapy and physiotherapy; facilities for chiropody, speech therapy and audiology; and occasionally music and art rooms. The day centre equivalents were medical or first-aid rooms, craft rooms, hairdressing and chiropody facilities and interview rooms.

Day hospitals generally had toilet and bathing facilities equipped for disabled people. Various types of medic baths or assisted showers were provided, sometimes equipped with hoists and other aids. Although some day centres had toilets for wheelchair users, a minority had bathing facilities; these were usually centres which catered for the more dependent elderly people.

Offices and staff accommodation were also more often found in statutory, full-time, purpose-built or adapted units which provided offices, staff rest rooms, changing rooms and toilets, various types of store room or utility room, and occasionally bases or office space for voluntary organisations or visiting professionals.

Problems with premises cited in the examples collected included buildings which were totally unsuitable or had structural defects; in such cases decisions had been made to change premises. More specific difficulties for day hospitals were the lack of treatment rooms, need for more or bigger rooms or storage space, or for improved facilities for therapeutic activities. Problems cited by SSD respondents were unsuitable toilets, the lack of separate rooms for activities, lack of storage space and of space generally. Clearly such difficulties can limit the extent to which units are able to undertake the activities necessary to meet their objectives.

Activities in day care units

Previous studies show that the level and diversity of activities were highest in day hospitals[9]; that staff in SSD day centres aimed to meet positive objectives through a range of components, but voluntary day centres and homes for elderly people had a lower level of activities[10]; and that voluntary staff tended to see the centre as a rest centre with the meal and company being ends in themselves.[11] Criticisms of day care activities concern their undemanding and repetitive nature. Hazan found no continuity or pattern in the daily round of repetitive songs, games and jokes; the members avoided any disturbance in the day centre culture they had evolved.[12] Users' participation in managing units was, as mentioned above, limited. On the other hand, Osborn noted that users were sometimes cajoled into activities that they did not enjoy.[13]

Day centres, largely used by working-class people, are somewhat stigmatised partly because they stem from welfare legislation. Writers and seminar participants stressed that activities should be suitable for both men and women and cater for many intellectual and cultural interests if day centres are to attract a wider range of people. Some projects have attempted this. One East Anglian day centre had a separate crafts room where an ambitious range of work was supervised by a craft instructor seconded by the SSD.[14] Another centre, the base for a theatre company, was used as a day centre which elderly members ran in addition to working as volunteers for the theatre.[15] An action project arranged visits by day centre members to a library; this led to increased self-confidence and interests for the members and greater mutual understanding between the staff.[16] The use of library deposit collections was studied in another day centre; it was found that members wanted a wider range of books and that books and welfare information leaflets should be easily accessible throughout the day.[17]

The introduction of more stimulating programmes, however, requires facilities and equipment, and the commitment and interest of staff. Further, users' attitudes may militate against change. For example, at a Norfolk day centre a new organiser described having to contend with a powerful group of bingo enthusiasts while introducing more varied activities. Such factors must be considered when planning programmes.

Where programmes are devised for individual users, they are often based on reasons for referral to the unit. Several SSD documents emphasised that individual and group activities should be geared to individual needs; for example, 'The work within the centre will have a social/community focus and will be formulated to take into account each individual care programme' (guidelines for a Westminster SSD day centre).

Hours of opening for day hospitals were usually from 8.30 a.m. or 9.00 a.m. to 4.30 p.m. or 5.00 p.m., with some units having a slightly longer or shorter day and, exceptionally, units open for less than five days a week. A few day hospitals opened for seven days a week regularly or as necessary. In one innovative project, a day hospital opened on Saturdays as a day centre with nursing staff and volunteers.[18] Many local authority day centres opened from Monday to Friday with opening hours slightly shorter than for day hospitals, and a few were open for seven days a week. Examples were also given of day care places available seven days a week in elderly people's homes and of day centres open for club activities in the evening. Voluntary sector day centres tended to open for two or three days a week, typically from 10.00 a.m. to 4.00 p.m., although some operated five days a week or more.

Users were not necessarily present throughout the hours of opening, especially where long journeys meant mid-morning arrivals and mid-afternoon departures. Examples suggest that most users were present for a maximum of five to six hours. However, in the interests of carers in full-time work, some units had nursing and care staff available from 8.00 a.m. to 7.00 p.m. so that users could be catered for early and late in the day.

A cooked meal was a feature of all types of day unit and was perceived as the focus of the day by volunteers and users in voluntary day centres.[19] The typical pattern outlined by statutory authorities was for users to have a hot drink on arrival, coffee and biscuits mid-morning, lunch followed by a cup of tea, and tea and biscuits before leaving. In some day centres drinks and snacks were on sale at coffee bars throughout the day. Commentators have suggested that users might participate more by organising the provision of their own meal but this was rare in practice. Day hospital meals were generally prepared in the main hospital kitchen, while in day centres meals were cooked on the premises or brought in from a variety of sources including meals on wheels kitchens.

Turning to the actual activities in day units, we recognise that a brief review cannot accurately reflect the relative importance, quality or extent of use of each component. We have categorised the activities as therapeutic, medical, service and social activities, although such distinctions are inevitably blurred in practice.

Studies have shown that even in day hospitals *therapeutic activities* were not well developed, although they were more formally therapeutic than those in day centres. Some very basic comparisons may be made for illustration from the information sent by statutory authorities.

Of the therapeutic activities mentioned in day hospitals nearly one-third were occupational therapy, slightly less were physiotherapy, and just over one-fifth speech therapy. Other activities were more specialised: reminiscence therapy, reality orientation, art or music therapy, and psychotherapy. Occupational therapy included monitoring, assessment, rehabilitation and prevention, and occasional home visits. Physiotherapy comprised walking therapy, exercises, group therapy, heat treatment and wax baths. A report on a West Essex HA day hospital showed that a high proportion of occupational therapy was maintenance therapy, and that three-quarters of those receiving physiotherapy had walking therapy.

In day centres only one-tenth of therapeutic activities were described as occupational therapy, physiotherapy or speech therapy. One-third of such activities were crafts and arts, and one-fifth were music and movement or keep-fit exercises. Other therapeutic activities were training in daily living skills, reminiscence, reality orientation, activities for those hard of hearing, drama, stroke group, relaxation, social rehabilitation and light industrial work.

Medical treatments and procedures were given, as expected, mainly in day hospitals. Nursing care or treatment comprised over one-quarter of such activity. Another quarter consisted of medical assessment, treatment or supervision. The remaining categories were drug therapy, dressings, pathology, X-ray, consultations and examinations, psychology, injections, enemata, stoma care, catheterisation and surgical appliances. Of such medical treatments and services only nursing care and treatment and supervision of medication were cited in day centres.

Other health, personal care, and advice services were offered in day units. About one-half of such services mentioned in day hospitals were health services, the most frequent being chiropody, followed by dietetics, dentistry, audiology and ophthalmology. In day centres such health services comprised about one-quarter of the services mentioned; chiropody was again the most frequent, then ophthalmology, dentistry, audiology and dietetics. One-half of the services cited in day centres were personal care services, with hairdressing the most frequent, followed by bathing, toileting and feeding, shopping, laundry and manicure. Such activities comprised about one-quarter of the services given in day hospitals, hairdressing being much the most frequent. Advice, information and counselling constituted about one-quarter of the services offered in day hospitals and day centres, and included access to social workers, advice for carers, welfare rights and health education.

The *social activities* cited in day units were as expected more diverse in day centres than in day hospitals which usually considered these as general social and diversional activities. Games including bingo, cards, dominoes and quizzes, formed the largest category of day centre social activities, followed by music, singing and entertainment, and discussions, current affairs and speakers. Together these activities comprised one-half of those mentioned. Other activities were outings and social events; sports such as bowls and billiards; adult education; gardening, plants and flower arranging; reading; socialising and conversation; visiting members in hospital; and watching television. Earlier studies stressed the importance of opportunities for opting out of activities and of separate space for reading or conversation, but these were rarely mentioned by authorities in response to CPA's letter.

These various components and activities were combined into a daily or weekly programme. Day hospitals tended to have a timetable for different group therapies each morning and afternoon which continued for the majority while individual patients were taken for assessments and treatments. Day centres placed less emphasis on individual treatment and therapy and more on group programmes. For example, Barnet SSD suggested a typical programme designed to maintain and improve functioning which included five or six activities each weekday. In the voluntary sector and also in many statutory day centres it is likely that programmes would be less varied.

Staffing and training

Day units' ability to offer suitable programmes depends on the resources available and on the quality and training of staff. Earlier studies suggested that day units were not always appropriately staffed to meet their objectives. Authorities' policy documents often contained statements about multi-disciplinary teams of staff, but in reality staff shortages meant that unqualified therapy assistants undertook professional roles as professionals were only occasionally available. Staff in SSD day centres have lower pay and status than fieldworkers.

A shortage of remedial therapy staff and inadequate staffing levels have been widely reported in research studies. Fennell and his colleagues observed that, 'Staffing levels may not permit much in the way of activities beyond attending to the users' needs while the users sit and chat'.[20] Information sent to CPA included similar comments. A report of discussions by centre social workers in Southwark found that the staffing establishment was inadequate and that there were considerable differences between the 13 centres in the levels of domestic staff.

Health authorities' documents show a typical pattern for day hospital staffing. Consultants with overall responsibility attended for one or two sessions a week and were available if needed. Registrars, senior house officers or clinical assistants attended for more frequent sessions and were also available on call. Most day hospitals had one full-time sister or charge nurse, one or two full- or part-time staff nurses and one or two nursing auxiliaries. Therapy staff consisted of three or four full- or part-time occupational therapists (OTs) and OT helpers and slightly fewer physiotherapists and helpers. Speech therapists were rarely on the regular staff; they attended for sessions or were available when needed, as were chiropodists, social workers and clinical psychologists. Most day hospitals had a receptionist/clerk and a domestic assistant; other services were provided by the main hospital.

The core staff of day centres often comprised a manager/organiser/officer-in-charge and a deputy, several care assistants and one or two domestic staff. Less frequently, centre staff included a cook or catering assistant, an instructor, drivers/attendants, a caretaker/handyperson, a receptionist/clerk and very occasionally a social worker or occupational therapist. The manager or organiser played a key role, particularly where, in the voluntary sector, this was the only paid post. In Wiltshire community-based voluntary centres the organiser was appointed by the management committee in consultation with the SSD.

Little information was available on the numbers of volunteers in day units. A survey of Oxfordshire day hospitals found that one-half used volunteers. Examples given at the Exeter seminar included one day centre run by a voluntary committee with paid staff and a rota of 40 volunteers; another totally voluntary village centre, open once a week, supervised by two chairmen, had 60 volunteers, each of whom worked once a month.

Although volunteers had a marginal role in statutory day units, their function was much more central in the voluntary sector. Several SSDs commented, in policy documents, on the role of volunteers, especially in centres funded by the local authority. For example, Wiltshire SSD's policy on community-based day centres states that, 'There will be a need for volunteers with a variety of skills who can be drawn from the local community as well as from Age Concern, the WRVS and British Red Cross. Volunteers would be able to contract for a part or the whole of a day session'. Other authorities commented on the difficulties of replacing older volunteers who were recruited when centres opened and eventually became unable to do the work.

The lack of training for paid and volunteer staff in day centres was cited by many writers as an obstacle to development of services. Service providers often claimed that the crucial factor was the caring nature of the worker. Others, however, emphasised that training was needed to promote positive attitudes to older people and ensure that workers did not patronise users or prevent them from acting for themselves.

Day hospital staff were more likely than those in day centres to have received professional or in-service training. Day hospitals themselves served as important training units for student professionals. Training for students and other visitors was sometimes offered at day centres but generally on an informal basis. The Certificate in Social Service (CSS) is the only nationally recognised course available to day centre workers. The Social Care Association (Education), Local Government Training Board and London Boroughs Training Committee offer courses for day centre managers and staff. In-service training is provided by SSDs for day unit staff and sometimes for volunteers. Such training, described in policy documents, includes short induction programmes, day release courses, short courses on welfare rights, management courses and creative skills courses.

During in-service training visits were arranged to local day units and other resources, for example home care and community nursing staff. Authorities such as Wiltshire SSD encouraged regular meetings of neighbouring day unit managers and staff. Other SSDs arranged visits by OTs or craft instructors to statutory and voluntary day centres to share their expertise. Regular support and supervision are also essential for staff in a potentially stressful occupation, but few authorities mentioned this in policy documents.

Apart from training, guidance is also available from publications. An illustrated *Good practice guide* was based on the East Anglia study findings.[21] Age Concern Scotland publishes *Centre forward*, a pack for those starting day centres for older people.[22] A recent book, *Day centres for the elderly*, also gives information on various aspects of setting up day centres.[23]

Costs and funding
The main costs of the services outlined above comprise staff payments, volunteers' expenses, rent and rates, heating and lighting, administration, catering and transport costs, plus capital costs of buildings and equipment. There are substantial differences in day care costs between and within types of day care service. Knapp and Missiakoulis found that units run by the NHS had higher costs than other day care units.[24] Challis and Davis showed that the estimated daily cost of SSD day care per user was nearly three times as much in a purpose-built day centre as in residential homes.[25] Examples sent to CPA revealed large differences, for example in rental costs, between similar

day units in the same sector. There were wide variations between authorities in the level of spending on day care services.

Elaine Murphy stressed that day hospital care was expensive, and Martin and Millard questioned whether it gave value for money.[26,27] The East Anglia study found that more expensive units had more users, opened for longer each day and more days each week, and offered more facilities than less expensive ones.[28] We shall return to the question of cost-effectiveness in chapter 8.

It is fairly difficult to obtain accurate information on costs of day care services since data are not recorded consistently. Some SSDs cannot easily cost day care separately from residential care. The costs of NHS day services may exclude ambulance transport costs. There may be hidden subsidies to the voluntary sector such as use of SSD premises or transport. Few authorities sent data on costs in response to CPA's trawl. Some examples are given below for illustration although they cannot be considered representative.

Revenue costs per annum were, for example, £121,888 for St Richard's day hospital, Chichester, and £183,536 for Williams day hospital, West Essex; staff costs accounted for 59% and 58% respectively, ambulance costs 26% and 24%, and non-pay costs 15% and 18%. An analysis of 13 SSD day centres in Southwark showed annual budgets ranging from £30,541 to £88,439 in 1987. Actual expenditure for 1984–85 for two SSD day centres in Kensington and Chelsea was £84,571 and £86,072. In Somerset mini-day care centres run by volunteers the overall costs of rent, equipment and transport were approximately £1,000 to £1,200 a year. Costs per attendance day were, for example, £40.80 in St Richard's day hospital, £11.15 and £23.24 in Kensington and Chelsea day centres, and ranged from £2.56 to £12.63 in Southwark day centres.

Day care services also varied in the extent to which users contributed to the costs. In day hospitals there was generally no charge to users whereas in SSD day centres the charge was set by the local authority, for example at £1.25 per day including meal and transport. The operational guidelines for Wiltshire community-based voluntary day centres stipulated that 'suitable charges should be made to members . . . based on the principle that they would feel that they have a personal stake in their day centre'. Age Concern day centres in different areas cited attendance charges of £1.00 or £1.25. A day centre run by a private trust, described at the Exeter seminar, charged £3.00 per day, but the SSD would subsidise low income users by £1.50.

Day hospitals are usually funded entirely by the NHS, and SSD day care in centres and homes is funded by the local authority, with some income from users. But some units, statutory and voluntary, whether attached to day hospitals or day centres, are wholly or partly funded through NHS joint finance. Funding sources for day centres run by voluntary agencies include grant aid from local authorities, joint finance, central government-sponsored funding, fundraising and donations, and charges. If the Griffiths report recommendations were implemented, the SSD would have specific grants from central government for community care, including day care, and would become responsible for funding projects currently joint financed.[29]

Examples were received of voluntary day centre funding. Wiltshire SSD provided initial setting-up grants to community-based centres, then an annual maintenance grant to cover organiser's pay and premises' costs. Northamptonshire SSD provided eight grants for voluntary day centres from £3,178 to £61,000 and a further ten grants under £1,000. The ten voluntary day centres in Croydon received heating and mileage allowances and grant aid from local authorities, income from donations, fundraising and sales, and charges. One-half of these day centres experienced difficulty raising sufficient funding.

There were marked variations in levels of funding between local authorities, some giving substantial amounts, others only token grants. Where day units relied on fundraising this could affect the type of activities undertaken; as Fennell and his colleagues pointed out, craft work tended to be limited to items which could easily be sold but gave little therapeutic benefit to users, for example knitted dishcloths.[30]

Apart from underfunding, the unpredictability of funding was a serious problem. Where the main source was grant aid from local or central government for fixed terms, much energy had to be diverted into negotiating the renewal of funding. Averil

Osborn expressed concern about the effects of short-term funding through central government schemes.[31] Decisions on such funding were often made at short notice and organisations were expected to take it up immediately. This uncertainty made it very difficult to plan services and retain or appoint staff. Difficulties also arose when the funding ended; local authorities were not always willing or able to take it over. Funding problems have sometimes been overcome by setting up joint projects or partnerships between the statutory and voluntary sectors.

Coordination between sectors in day care services is discussed in chapter 6. First, we describe briefly seven different types of day unit from the case studies, to illustrate how the various components of day care services are combined in practice.

Case studies
1. Psychogeriatric day hospital
Greenwood psychogeriatric day hospital is situated within a large psychiatric hospital administered by Waltham Forest health authority. The day unit began operation as a day hospital in 1974; managerial responsibility is held by the unit general manager (mental health) and professional responsibility by two consultants and a nursing officer. Greenwood occupies an adapted ground-floor unit with its own ramped entrance and entrance hall, two large activity areas for dining and sitting and for sitting and group activities, and smaller rooms, toilet facilities, and kitchen. Space is used flexibly, the large carpeted rooms subdivided by furniture to create a homely atmosphere.

The day hospital, staffed from 8.30 a.m. to 5.00 p.m. Monday to Friday, remains open until 6.30 p.m. if necessary. Although 40 places are designated, in practice 25 to 30 patients attend daily, on average twice a week each. The unit accepts people over 65 with functional or organic mental disorders. All referrals are directed through the consultants and there is no waiting list. Relatives and carers are involved in discussing treatment and care plans, and in a relatives' support group. There are no charges to users.

The objectives include treatment, assessment, observation and monitoring; prevention of in-patient admission; enabling early discharge; and providing respite care. Each patient's care plan/

treatment programme is decided by the multi-disciplinary team in discussion with the patient or, if appropriate, the relative, and each patient is allocated a trained nurse. The weekly programme of therapeutic activities includes reality orientation, reminiscence therapy, relaxation, support groups, and individual activities such as basket making and needlecraft. A short session of physical exercises is held each day. The afternoon ends with social activities including quizzes, music and pet therapy. During rest periods books and magazines are available.

On admission there is physical and mental assessment by doctors, nurses and occupational therapists. Patients are reviewed once a month. During the day individuals are called for assessment or treatment. Individual advice and counselling is given to patients and carers. Ophthalmic or dental treatment and chiropody are available if urgently needed, but staff consider such care more appropriately provided in the community. There is no hairdressing service.

Each psychogeriatric consultant holds a weekly inter-disciplinary review meeting. Senior house officers and clinical assistants attend for several sessions per week. The unit is staffed by a sister/charge nurse responsible for daily coordination, two staff nurses, two enrolled nurses, a nursing assistant, two occupational therapy assistants, one care assistant, two part-time secretaries, a part-time orderly, and two volunteers for weekly manicure and pet therapy. Doctors, nursing officers, occupational therapist, senior social worker, senior psychologist and community psychiatric nurse are available when needed.

Most patients are brought by ambulance services, booked by telephone by the secretaries. Although fairly satisfactory, the services are unable to guarantee collection times which may start at 8.00 a.m. although most users do not arrive until 10.00–10.30 a.m. Afternoon collection starts at 3.00 p.m. and may not finish until 6.30 p.m. Although most users enjoyed the day, once the first patients had been collected at 3.00 p.m., others became restless and anxious to go home, and there was little concentration on any activity.

2. Geriatric day hospital
Hastings health authority's St Helen's day hospital opened in 1965. Three geriatric consultants have professional responsi-

bility. The day hospital has its own entrance and is purpose-built as a wing of St Helen's hospital; the geriatricians' offices are situated between the main hospital and this wing. The premises consist of a very large central room with smaller treatment/assessment rooms including a kitchen, and a large physiotherapy area which can be partitioned off but is normally part of the large room.

The day hospital is open from 8.00 a.m. to 5.00 p.m. Monday to Friday for in-patients and from 10.00 a.m. to 3.30 p.m. for 32 day patients; on average 25 attend twice a week each for six to eight weeks but numbers fluctuate widely. Most users are physically handicapped elderly people; some, mainly stroke patients, are younger. Referrals are accepted from GPs or consultants, then all are assessed by a geriatrician. There is an attractive leaflet for patients and relatives who are encouraged to participate in discussing individual care plans. Services are free of charge to users. In 1986 the cost per day place, including salaries and premises, was £27.16.

The multi-disciplinary team takes a holistic approach, with the aim of rehabilitation combined with medical and nursing care after in-patient treatment or to avoid hospital admission. In the morning patients receive physiotherapy, occupational therapy and speech therapy. Lunch is followed by a quiet rest then a short exercise session. Other group activities include reality orientation, quizzes, memory games, cooking and gardening groups, and social activities which contribute to patients' care plans, for example a tea party to practise domestic skills. Consultants, nurses and therapists carry out individual treatment and assessment during the day. Nursing care includes monitoring, and teaching self-medication, but not community nursing roles. Chiropody is offered once a fortnight; dentist, dietician and stoma care nurse are available if needed. No hairdressing is provided but patients are put in touch with a home hairdresser. Social workers may give individual advice or counselling, and leaflets on welfare rights and other topics are available.

There is a weekly case conference for each consultant, attended by the hospital team, community physiotherapist, health visitor for the elderly, and other community professionals. Staff meetings are held every morning about patient care and monthly about work problems. Registrars and senior house officers attend for sessions and are on call. The coordinator/head occupational therapist, staff nurse, two enrolled nurses, part-time physiotherapist, part-time speech therapist, receptionist, technical instructor and porter are based in the day hospital. Three OTs (including the coordinator/head OT) and eight OT helpers (three part-time) work both in the main and day hospitals. A volunteer helps once a week making coffee and chatting with patients. Staff are very positive about the unit and the patients are happy to attend.

The day hospital has exclusive use of two ambulances during morning and afternoon journey times. There are 26 places for the town catchment area and six for the country area. Within these numbers the receptionist makes detailed requests and the transport section plans the journeys. Patients have to be ready by 8.30 a.m. because the collection rota varies. Journeys could take an hour and sometimes those who suffered from travel sickness were offered a voluntary car if they could use it. Few other transport difficulties were reported.

3. Purpose-built SSD day centre for elderly and elderly mentally ill people
Crossroads day centre, opened in 1985, is run by Norfolk SSD in its own premises next to an SSD residential home. It has an officer-in-charge, and links with the SSD area office. The centre is fully accessible to wheelchair users. It has a large activities room, kitchen, bathrooms and toilets, laundry, office, medical and hairdressing rooms. Linked by corridor is a new day unit for elderly mentally ill people (EMI) with a large activities room; some facilities are shared with the main unit.

The centre, open Monday to Friday from 9.00 a.m. to 5.00 p.m., has 40 places in the main unit and 20 in the EMI unit. A total of 43 to 55 users attend each day, 12 daily but most once or twice weekly. Referrals are made through social workers who visit the client and negotiate attendance. The officer-in-charge also visits after referral, and clients and relatives are offered a visit to the centre. Users are charged £1.15 per day plus 22p for the transport.

The objectives are social stimulation and relief for carers, especially of EMI users. The EMI unit does reality orientation and reminiscence, and the same activities as the main unit, although for shorter periods. Some social activities are held jointly. All users do crafts, such as needlecrafts, painting, and making goods for the bazaar. Adult education courses such as cookery are offered and books are supplied by the library. Nursing care, chiropody, bathing and hairdressing are available. After lunch, provided by the meals on wheels kitchen on site, there is an hour of quizzes, word games or discussions for mental stimulation. Ice cream and sweets are sold in the shop. Music and movement is offered weekly and a physiotherapist visits regularly. Social activities include bingo, card games, dominoes, visits by entertainers, outings, supermarket shopping, and sherry parties for birthdays.

The centre is staffed by the officer-in-charge and her deputy, three full-time and four part-time care assistants (one full- and two part-time for the EMI unit), three part-time drivers and one part-time domestic worker. There are no clerical workers and no volunteers. A weekly staff meeting is held. The officer-in-charge aims to widen the responsibilities of care assistants, who have attended a creative activity course arranged by the SSD and DHA. The officer-in-charge and deputy attended a mental health course and there was a training day before the EMI unit opened and another after 12 months. Short courses on lifting and continence management were attended.

The unit has three tail-lift ambulances, each of which brings users from a different part of the town, sometimes making two trips. To avoid long journeys by ambulance, users from the villages are brought in by taxi, which is a cost-effective method, costing less than using voluntary drivers. Users are normally at the centre from 9.45 a.m. to 4.00 p.m. and enjoy attending, although some bingo enthusiasts initially resisted the wider range of activities introduced by the new officer-in-charge.

4. SSD day centre in an adapted building
Clydach day centre, Cardiff, is administered by South Glamorgan SSD and has a salaried organiser. The centre, established in 1964, is held in an adapted, rather dilapidated building which also houses community and voluntary organisations using their own rooms and a large meeting hall on the first floor. The day centre's ground-floor premises comprise kitchen and servery, dining/sitting room, one end of which is

carpeted and has easy chairs, and small TV room/men's sitting room. Women's toilets are on the first floor and there are three stairs down to the men's toilets, also used by women who cannot manage stairs. There is an office on the first floor.

The 60-place centre is open Monday to Friday, 9.00 a.m. to 5.00 or 6.00 p.m., with an average attendance of 45 fit elderly people. Most attend each day, apart from 15 transport users who attend twice weekly. Clients refer themselves or are referred by doctors, health visitors or social workers, or recruited personally by the organiser. Users participate by suggesting outings and running raffles. They pay 13p for coffee on arrival and 75p for lunch.

The service aims to provide a social setting, enable people to get out of the house and have social contacts. Activities are mainly social, including monthly outings paid for by users and from raffle money, and Easter and Christmas parties. Sequence dancing is held weekly, and bingo played three times a week with local pensioners' groups who use the centre. There is little therapeutic activity and no chiropody, bathing or hairdressing services. The organiser, however, gives information and advice, refers people to appropriate help, including contacting a social worker if necessary, and carries out minor hearing aid repairs. The Centre also runs a 'meals on legs' service for the local area, to cover short-term needs for meals.

At present the full-time organiser also supervises two other day centres but this is under review. Two cooks and two assistant cooks work alternate days, and a cleaner works five days a week. Staff meetings are held daily. There are also seven volunteers: two men to carry trays of lunches, and five women who collect money or serve coffees and meals. The paid and voluntary staff enjoy the relaxed atmosphere of the centre. The main difficulty is uncertainty over the future of the rather unsuitable building, which needs to be renovated or changed.

Transport is provided twice a week by Voluntary Emergency Social Transport (VEST), a voluntary organisation funded by the local authority, which uses an adapted vehicle with a tail-lift. The organiser arranges the rota with VEST. Although the service is reliable, the 15 places per day offered are not sufficient. Collection times are unpredictable. Users are ready by 9.30

91

a.m. but may not be collected until 11.00 a.m., and the return pick-up time is between 2.00 and 3.30 p.m., which can mean a very short day at the centre. Actual journey times are 20 to 30 minutes; some users enjoy the journey but others do not. Users like the centre's informal atmosphere and enjoy a chat and 'bargain' lunch.

5. A day centre in an SSD residential home
Wiltshire SSD's Watermead is a purpose-built elderly person's home opened in 1986 with an integrated day unit providing 'primary' day care for dependent elderly people. The officer-in-charge of the home is responsible for the day unit. The home is attractively designed and fully accessible, with a courtyard and pleasant grounds. The day unit has a medium-sized sitting room with armchairs around the walls, an adjoining craft store room, and shared use of the other facilities of the home such as bathrooms equipped for disabled people, and hairdressing room, together with use of the dining room and general lounge areas.

The day centre is open six days a week from 9.30 a.m. to 3.45 p.m. Ten places are available on Monday and Saturday, and 20 places on Tuesday to Friday. The unit caters for frail, physically handicapped and mentally infirm elderly people from the community, and for residents, some of whom are receiving respite care. Some confused members also attend a health authority day unit; a community psychiatric nurse liaises between the two units. Some other users also attend 'secondary' day care units in the community. Users are placed by a social worker, and the day care organiser attends allocation meetings. Users pay 75p for meals and 40p for transport.

The day unit's main objectives are social: to provide socialisation, meals, and a place to go. Therapeutic activity consists mainly of needlecrafts on which the women spend most of their time while chatting in the lounge. High quality work is produced for sale. The men are reluctant to enter the lounge, deterred by the preponderance of women, and usually sit in the lobby area of the home, watching TV and smoking. Lunch is served in the dining room with the residents. Medical and other services offered include simple dressings, chiropody, bathing and hairdressing. Social outings are arranged. There is a visiting library service which is valued. Activities seem less varied and stimulating than in other centres and there are few activities that seem to engage the men.

The day unit staff, a full-time day centre organiser and two part-time care assistants who work alternate mornings and afternoons, are members of the home's team. Staff meetings are held for all workers. This integrated approach was viewed positively by staff. Day unit staff work in the home if necessary and the home staff work in the day unit so that holiday cover is easily arranged with familiar staff members available. There is one volunteer, a driver.

Non-resident users are brought in by a community minibus or by the voluntary driver using his own car. Users find the minibus rather uncomfortable but like the friendly driver. They have no complaints about lengthy journey times and compete to be the last home because they enjoy the trip around the villages. Users seem very satisfied with the centre to which they come for the company and the meal, and they like the facilities, especially the hairdressing.

6. Rural day centre run by a voluntary organisation
The Beckford Friday Club is an example of Wiltshire's 'secondary' or community day care for less dependent elderly people. It was founded by Age Concern Wiltshire community development officers with a setting-up grant from Wiltshire SSD. It has an organiser responsible to the centre's management committee on which the local community is represented. The club is one of several held in an adapted redundant small hospital building, the Beckford centre, which is accessible to disabled people and has various rooms used by clubs and community groups. The day centre uses the original day room of the hospital, comprising a large sitting/dining area with adjoining kitchen/servery.

This day club is open every Friday from 10.00 a.m. to 4.00 p.m. and has 32 members from the small town and two nearby villages. Users are fairly fit elderly people but include some who are frail, handicapped, housebound or lonely. About 20 to 25 attend each week, some of whom also attend primary day care centres or pensioners' clubs. There is no waiting list. People over retirement age apply direct, or referrals are made to the organiser by GPs, health visitors or social workers. The organiser selects members, in consultation with a professional worker where appropriate. The centre receives an annual maintenance grant from the SSD to cover the organiser's pay and premises costs. Total annual cost is approximately £1,200. Users pay 75p for lunch and 40p for transport.

The objectives of the centre are to provide social contact, social and mental stimulation, companionship and a hot meal, and relief for carers. The organiser is keen to provide stimulating activities and there is a lively atmosphere with members busily involved and talking. Therapeutic activities include exercise and yoga, and games such as skittles. Quizzes are held, and scrabble and whist played after lunch, which is supplied by a local SSD residential home. There are outings once a month during the summer. Raffles are held to raise funds, and cards, stamps and groceries are sold. Advice and information are offered on welfare rights and services.

As in other community day centres in Wiltshire, the part-time organiser receives an honorarium, currently £660 per annum. All other staff are volunteers, five of whom regularly help in the centre, serve meals, chat with members and help with activities. There are no difficulties in recruiting volunteers who are mainly younger retired people. As yet there is little training for staff but SSD officers are encouraging the initiation of joint meetings for organisers of Beckford and neighbouring day centres.

Volunteers also drive the transport which consists of one community minibus which is purpose-built with a tail-lift. Journeys are not long because the policy is for members to live within seven miles and within a 40 minute journey time. A further minibus would help to get all members into the centre earlier but there would be difficulty staffing it with volunteer drivers. Members and volunteers enjoyed their day at the centre, especially the company and the lunch.

7. Urban voluntary agency day centre for older people from ethnic minorities
Navjivan, a project of Age Concern Leicester, runs a day centre for frail elderly Asian people. Established in 1982, the centre is held at Preston Lodge, a purpose-built SSD home for elderly people. The day centre uses the first floor of one wing of the

home. There is lift access to the unit. The premises are provided free by the local authority.

The day centre is open from Monday to Friday, 10.30 a.m. to 4.30 p.m., with 20 places available, and mostly filled, each day. Users are all Asians, four or five from the home, the others from the community, and are physically handicapped or mentally infirm.

The majority attend every day and all attend on most days. All users are assessed by social workers; most referrals come through the SSD, although some originate from the health authority. There are enough Asian language speaking social workers to carry out the assessments and users are allocated social workers if needed. Users and carers are not yet involved in running the centre; the project officer is starting a relatives' support group in conjunction with the neighbourhood care team. Users pay £1.25 per day for meals and transport.

The centre aims to provide a homely venue for users, and relief for carers, and to offer a day care service which is sensitive to the cultural, religious and language needs of Asian elders and is thus more appropriate than traditional models. After arrival and a cup of tea, some users enjoy singing religious songs using traditional instruments, while others play cards, then all members play board games. A freshly cooked, high-standard vegetarian lunch is followed by a rest period, then users watch a video. Occasional outings are arranged. Magazines are available and the project worker helps with reading and writing letters, as most users are illiterate. Each Thursday the day centre can call on a social worker who holds a surgery in the home. Users' individual social workers also visit the day centre and a community nurse from the adjacent centre is called in if needed.

There are two full-time staff: the project officer whose salary is funded by Leicester SSD and whose line manager is an assistant director of Age Concern Leicester; and the organiser whose post is currently funded by the Inner Areas Programme. There are two regular volunteers, and also 15 MSC-funded community programme workers distributed between several projects. Monthly staff meetings are held for all staff, and the MSC supervisor and project officer provide in-service training. The lack of paid permanent staff, heavy dependence on volunteers, and uncertainty about funding, to some extent inhibit the development of the centre and of staff training.

Navjivan raised £1,600 towards the cost of a vehicle which is run by Age Concern Leicester. The project officer organises a rota for transport. Journey times are short because the geographical area covered is small. Transport is reliable except when the vehicle is borrowed by other centres. Users and carers are very appreciative of the centre's services and would like seven days a week opening.

Components of day care services
These brief case studies illustrate the diversity of day care services. In chapter 6 we examine how such services are coordinated and how they fit with the wider community care scene. First, we summarise below features of the key components of day care services described in the present chapter.

1. Management and control
Location of day unit staff within service provider's management
structure.
Centralised or local control of individual day care units.
Management committees for individual units.
Administrative responsibility and accountability.
Professional responsibility and accountability.
Key workers for individual users.
Formal communication systems eg. regular meetings.
Participation by users in running units.
Participation by relatives and carers.
Complaints procedures.

2. Premises
Location and ownership of premises.
Purpose-built, adapted or general purpose.
Exclusive or shared use.
External access for disabled people: level access, ramps, rails.
Internal access and circulation space for disabled people.
Environment: decor, furnishings, views, garden.
Flexibility in use of space.
Main activity, sitting, dining and kitchen areas.
Treatment and therapy areas, facilities for chiropody,
hairdressing.
Toilet and bathing facilities suitable for disabled people.

Entrance and reception areas, staff offices and facilities, storage space.

3. Activities

Opening hours include early morning/evening/weekend.
Daily/weekly programme of activities.
Programmes for individual users.
Range of intellectual and cultural activities suitable for men and women.
Therapeutic activities, eg. occupational and physiotherapy.
Medical treatments and procedures.
Health and personal care services eg. chiropody, bathing, hairdressing.
Advice, information and counselling.
Social activities eg. games, music, discussions, outings.
Meals. Participation by users in preparation.
Availability of drinks and snacks during the day.

4. Staffing and training

Staffing levels adequate to meet objectives.
Roles of paid staff and volunteers.
Availability of professional staff, care staff, organisers and administrative staff, domestic staff, drivers and escorts.
Recruitment of volunteers.
Training for paid and volunteer staff.
Visits and meetings for local day unit staff.
Support and supervision for staff.
Guidance on day unit practice.

5. Costs and funding

Capital costs: buildings and equipment.
Revenue costs: staffing, volunteers' expenses, rent and rates, heating and lighting, administration, catering, transport.
Income from charges to users.
Direct funding of own units by HAs and SSDs.
NHS joint finance.
LA grant aid to voluntary organisations.
Central government-sponsored funding.
Fundraising and donations.

REFERENCES
1. See for example E.M. Goldberg and N. Connelly, *The effectiveness of social care for the elderly*, Policy Studies Institute, London, 1982, pp 133–34

2. J. Carter, *Day services for adults—somewhere to go*, George Allen and Unwin, London, 1981

3. G. Fennell, A.R. Emerson, M. Sidell and A. Hague, *Day centres for the elderly in East Anglia*, University of East Anglia School of Economic and Social Studies, Norwich, 1981

4. D. Leat, S. Tester and J. Unell, *A price worth paying? A study of the effects of government grant aid to voluntary organisations*, Policy Studies Institute, London, 1986

5. D. Heptinstall, Handing back the power, *Community care*, 405, 1982, 10–12

6. H. Hazan, *The limbo people*, Routledge and Kegan Paul, London, 1980

7. V. Bacon and M. Dubber, *Buildings used for the day care of elderly people*, Oxford Polytechnic, Oxford, 1987

8. Fennell *et al*, *Day centres for the elderly*

9. Fennell *et al*, *Day centres for the elderly*

10. R. Bowl, H. Taylor, M. Taylor and N. Thomas, *Day care for the elderly in Birmingham*, University of Birmingham Social Services Unit, Birmingham, 1978

11. Carter, *Day services for adults*

12. Hazan, *The limbo people*

13. A. Osborn, *Day care for older people in day centres*, Age Concern Scotland, Edinburgh, 1985

14. Fennell *et al*, *Day centres for the elderly*

15. Drama down at the day centre, *New Age*, 2, 1978, 25–28

16. D. Runnicles and G. Woodcroft, Promoting the interest of elderly people, *Social Services Research*, 14, 4, 1985, 37–48

17. M. Simes, B. Anderson, J. Bowen, R. Steel, *Do books still matter? The library and information needs of the elderly in community day centres*, School of Librarianship, Leeds Polytechnic and School of Business and Social Studies, Bradford College, Bradford, 1980

18. A. Dobbs and A. Clayton, Empty Saturdays come to life, *The Health Service Journal*, 98, 5034, 1987

19. Carter, *Day services for adults*

20. Fennell *et al*, *Day centres for the elderly*, p 201

21. G. Fennell and M. Sidell, *Good practice guide—day centres for the elderly*, Centre for East Anglian Studies, Norwich, 1982

22. Age Concern Scotland, *Centre forward: a step by step guide to starting a day centre for older people*, Age Concern Scotland, Edinburgh, 1984

23. V. Grant and J. Williams, *Day centres for the elderly: how to set up, organise and run a day centre for elderly people*, Benton Bros, New Zealand, 1986

24. M. Knapp and S. Missiakoulis, Inter-sectoral cost comparisons: day care for the elderly, *Journal of Social Policy*, 11, 3, 1982, 335–54

25. D. Challis and B. Davis, *Case management in community care*, Gower Publishing, Aldershot, 1986

26. Murphy, Day care: who and what is it for?

27. A. Martin and P.H. Millard, *Day hospitals for the elderly: therapeutic or social?*, St George's Hospital, London, 1978

98

28. Fennell *et al, Day centres for the elderly*
29. R. Griffiths, *Community care: agenda for action*, HMSO, London, 1988
30. Fennell *et al, Day centres for the elderly*
31. Osborn, *Day care for older people*

6 Coordination of day care services

Introduction

In caring in the community for elderly people and others designated by the DHSS as priority groups, a major difficulty is the coordination of services and facilities for people whose needs span departmental and professional boundaries. Many writers have emphasised the necessity for coordination and collaboration in order to improve the effectiveness of services. In *Councils of Care* the Centre for Policy on Ageing illustrated the immense difficulties of implementing coordination of services for older people.[1]

Successful coordination implies commitment to working together at all levels, rather than paying lip service to the ideal, holding the occasional meeting or issuing a joint document. The many obstacles to coordination between statutory and voluntary agencies with different organisational structures include conflicts between departmental or professional interests. Further, when authorities are under immediate pressure and facing resource restraints it is difficult to devote sufficient time to long-term aims such as improving coordination, setting common objectives, and providing structures to facilitate different methods of joint working at operational level.

The findings of earlier research and of the present study clearly indicate that, where day care services are concerned, it is essential to pay more attention to coordination at policy, management and operational levels in various aspects of the services. First, both within and between sectors it is important to consider how day care should fit into the wider spectrum of community care services. Second, coordination between all the day care services operated by different sectors in a locality should be an objective. Third, coordination between the providers and staff of day care services, the users, and relatives or carers, should be an integral part of using day care to help support older people in the community. In this chapter we consider all these aspects of coordination and give examples of good practice which have attempted to overcome the difficulties in inter-agency collaboration.

Community care context

Many commentators have expressed concern over the issue of coordination at policy or operational levels between day care and other community care services. The Birmingham survey found problems at operational level; for example, referral agents did not supply centres with information on individual clients' needs, and did not continue visiting clients once a placement in a day unit had been made.[2] Osborn argued that 'day care must become part of a comprehensive care and support system' if day units were to be used appropriately; she suggested as an example the provision of services at day centres by the primary health care team.[3] Peace recommended developing links between the specialist hospital-based service for elderly mentally ill people, including a day hospital, and other hospital and community services.[4]

Poor coordination between day care and other community care services within the same agency was a particular problem where SSDs were concerned. The Birmingham study found both poor communication at policy level and inadequate communication of policy to fieldworkers.[5] Similarly, the NISW study found that day care workers were given insufficient support by departmental managers who showed little understanding of their work.[6] An Audit Commission report which found management weaknesses in some SSDs in providing social services for elderly people offered the following suggestion for using day care more effectively:

Authorities should satisfy themselves that the purpose of providing day care is widely understood and agreed throughout the department, that the nature of the service given is in line with its stated objectives and that appropriate attention is given to effective liaison with other organisations.[7]

A further issue related to inadequate coordination and communication is the isolation of day units, since other services' staff have little contact with or knowledge of them. To reduce the isolation of day care workers, joint meetings or training for staff of day units in a locality have been suggested (see chapter 5). Attendance at day units may also have an isolating effect on users, if they are taken from their immediate environment to another area to meet people they only see once or twice a week in a centre which has little contact with its own neighbourhood. On the basis of such findings commentators have recommended ways of integrating day units into their local community, for example by using them more widely as resource centres or bases for neighbourhood projects or 'meals on legs' schemes.

The desirability of considering individual services such as day care in the context of the rest of the user's life has led to increasing interest in the concept of a 'package' of community care, as now advocated by Griffiths.[8] Research such as the Birmingham study has shown that, in practice, when day care users received a number of different services these were not considered in relation to each other; Bowl and others commented, 'When one further considers that few referral agents had developed conscious alternatives to gaining a place for a client in a day centre, it is difficult to represent day care placements as forming part of a conscious "community care package" '.[9]

Recognising the practical difficulties of offering day care as part of a package, several writers have suggested developments. Goldberg and Connelly proposed four aspects of the integration of day care into a continuum of community services: information on local community resources; use of the case coordinator; clearer assessment of needs for day care; and regular monitoring.[10] Bayley and his colleagues pointed out the need for local control over residential and day care services if fieldworkers are to be able to select an appropriate package for an individual.[11] Tibbitt commented that there has been little research on the interrelationships between services, the implications for other services of receiving day care, or whether day care is an effective substitute for other services.[12]

All these aspects of the need for coordination in community care generally have been well documented, for example by the Audit Commission.[13] The publication of the review by Sir Roy Griffiths, set up in response to the Audit Commission's findings, engendered much discussion on the desirability and feasibility of implementing the Griffiths proposals for a clearer framework for inter-agency coordination and for joint planning. The review

called for stronger central government commitment to community care, for example by appointing a minister, and for local
authorities to become lead authorities in assessing needs and
organising the provision of community care services, as opposed
to purely 'health' services which would remain with the health
authority.[14] Several commentators have pointed out the difficulties of defining and separating 'health' services in this way.
Hunter and Judge expressed doubts about the willingness of
central government to provide policy leadership and delegate
responsibilities to local authorities, and about SSDs' ability to
take on these new tasks.[15]

Although day care is hardly mentioned specifically in the
Griffiths report, the recommendations propose that SSDs would
be responsible for assessing needs and arranging and managing
(by a care manager if appropriate) packages of care including
day care in various settings.[16] The day hospital would presum-
ably remain under the auspices of the health authority if defined
as having a mainly 'health' function, and would constitute one
of the range of services available in a community care package.
It also seems likely that the use of private residential homes for
day care and the private provision of day centres would increase
if Griffiths' proposals were implemented, since he advocated
that, 'The onus in all cases should be on the social services
authorities to show that the private sector is being fully stimu-
lated and encouraged'.[17]

Local and health authority collaboration in community care
Statutory arrangements for joint care planning between local
and health authorities include joint consultative committees
(JCCs), on which voluntary organisations have also been represented since 1984, and joint care planning teams (JCPTs). In
some areas services for elderly people have been reviewed by
working groups appointed by such bodies. Health authorities
have also had planning teams for elderly people, and more
recently joint planning teams with the local authority. Some
HAs and SSDs have reviewed services for elderly people in
preparing their own strategic planning documents.

Many joint or health or local authority documents detailing
such plans or reviews were sent in response to CPA's trawl.
Most stated policies in favour of care in the community and
aimed to help older people to live independently and respect

their rights and dignity. Some commented that community care was not a cheap option and should be adequately resourced. Most documents gave short profiles of the different community care services. For this study we were particularly interested in their content on coordination between and within agencies in providing community care for older people.

The need for improved communication and collaboration was recognised by many authorities. Solihull HA and Solihull metropolitan borough council, for example, considered one of the issues in the process of developing a joint strategy to be 'the need to develop better systems of communications between agencies at grass roots level in order to ensure that clients receive the most suitable packages of care'. Islington SSD, in considering a draft joint policy on the care of elderly people, stressed the need to increase understanding of community care and local support networks, and the crucial part to be played by inter-agency collaboration.

Some areas had particular difficulties. In Surrey, for example, services for elderly people were split between the county SSD, which provided home care, residential care, day care in residential homes, and social work support, and district councils, which provided meals on wheels, day centres and sheltered housing. A review of community care for elderly people by external auditors Coopers and Lybrand found a lack of collaboration as each authority fulfilled its own functions with little consideration for overall county policy; they recommended that the county council should take the lead role. The SSD's response to specific recommendations on liaison was that action and joint planning should be encouraged at county level but take place at operational level, the area/district.

Authorities also emphasised the need for joint planning and development of services; for example, a report by Staffordshire SSD on services for the elderly stated that, 'Joint planning between social services, health authorities and the voluntary sector in a systematic, fruitful and unified way is essential if a comprehensive, integrated network to serve elderly people and their families is to be developed'. Joint planning at local level was advocated, particularly by geographically widespread authorities such as Devon and Kent SSDs. Kent SSD area directors had each formulated three-year plans in consultation with local agencies; these plans had been developed into a county plan which would be adapted as circumstances changed, with an input from all agencies. Cheltenham and District HA stressed the importance of identifying a group of individuals who would develop, and review annually, written joint policies for the district.

Various components of an ideal joint plan were suggested in strategy documents and included identification of the needs of elderly people and carers; explicit criteria on eligibility for specific services; clarification of which agencies were appropriate to meet specific needs; common assessment procedures; dependence rating scales; consistent allocation of residential and hospital care places; discharge planning policy; and arrangements for financing and management of services.

A major objective of improved communication and joint planning was to develop an integrated service offering a continuum of care for elderly people. For example, the report of North Tees JCPT working group for elderly people recommended that, 'A joint approach between statutory agencies and voluntary organisations should be encouraged in providing a fully integrated and comprehensive service for the elderly'. Such approaches would make individually tailored care packages feasible in practice. Most of the strategic documents stated such policies which aimed to help dependent elderly people to remain at home and to support carers. Some authorities considered the implications of stating such aims. Shropshire HA, for instance, posed questions in its strategic plan about the balance of care: 'In the "Community" model, what should be the level of provision of day places, residential accommodation, and back-up services such as nursing staff, meals on wheels, domestic helps, physiotherapy, occupational therapy, audiology and speech therapy?'

Several strategic documents gave examples of the implementation of comprehensive services or of the input by one agency to services of another. Social services departments such as Humberside, Kent and South Glamorgan had reorganised their departmental structure so that residential, day care, domiciliary and fieldwork services were integrated under common management at local level. Bexley HA's aims included preventing disability and handicap by 'increasing the availability of geriatric assessment and treatment by the regular visits of specialist trained staff especially to day centres and part III homes'. Milton Keynes HA proposed to strengthen the community services and increase support to families and carers, day centres, residential homes and sheltered housing units.

Another method of facilitating integration and communication was to localise joint provision of services to elderly people. Some SSDs which had reorganised and integrated all services at local level were developing the concept of the resource centre. In Kent such centres were usually to be based in homes for elderly people and would 'organise for elderly people and their relatives coordinated programmes of services to meet their needs whether this is residential care, respite care, home care services, day activities or social work counselling'. Devon SSD's strategy proposed 'community resource centres' and South Glamorgan SSD is developing locally based 'elderly persons' support units'.

Assessment is a crucial aspect of the provision of individual care packages. Several strategic documents advocated assessment for a range of services to meet people's needs as a whole rather than assessment for a single service. Strategies of SSDs such as Leeds included assessment for all services offered by the department. Joint strategies often included multi-disciplinary assessment by professionals from different agencies, and the system of a care manager or key worker to coordinate services for dependent elderly people. South Tyneside's review of services for the elderly, for example, states that, 'One way to develop a multi-disciplinary team approach would be to have individual patient care programmes which would involve a team assessment of needs (including HA staff, GPs, social services and housing, together with voluntary agencies, carers and patients) followed by an identification of *how* these needs should be met and by *whom*. A named coordinator of action ("key worker") for each client would be required'. The importance of regular review or reassessment was also emphasised in strategy documents.

Coordination between sectors of day care provision

Commentators agree that day care for elderly people has mushroomed in various forms without a coordinated approach which might be described as a continuum of care to meet varied needs. Most studies found little consistent assessment across the sectors to allow cross-referrals; as a result elderly people tended to receive the service applied for rather than that most suited to their needs. For example, very dependent elderly people might be placed in voluntary day centres which did not have suitable facilities for them. Although there were exceptions, the studies found little liaison in planning or providing services between the different statutory and voluntary sectors.

The lack of liaison and jointly planned provision between day hospital and day centre providers had particular implications for day hospitals operating a short-term rehabilitation service. If patients could not be discharged to day centres at the end of their treatment, they either had to be kept in the day hospital on a long-term basis or be discharged and receive no day care. The need for closer cooperation between day hospitals and other day care provision was especially acute where older people with mental illness were concerned. As Peace pointed out, elderly people with depression or mild dementia do not need medical care in a day hospital but places in local authority day centres or joint-funded specialist centres.[18]

The Birmingham study called for 'a clearer definition of the roles of the various day care alternatives' and suggested that those responsible for the different day care sectors should meet to discuss these roles.[19] The researchers found a lack of liaison within the SSD which had different sections responsible for day care in day centres and in residential homes and another for liaison with voluntary centres: 'There are no regular formal meetings between them to discuss day care policy—nor are there with the providers of NHS day services'.[20]

Studies also revealed poor coordination between the SSD and the voluntary sector even when the local authority supported day centres with grant aid, for which there was very little financial accountability. The reluctance of SSDs to interfere in voluntary organisations' work was considered inappropriate by, for example, the East Anglia researchers who considered that SSDs should take a more active role in advising voluntary organisations.[21]

Coordination difficulties reported by authorities in response to CPA's trawl included general observations about low levels of integration between health and social services day care, and between statutory and voluntary services. In Coventry, for example, a joint working party commented that, 'Segments of day care cannot exist in isolation from each other; interdependency which is conceptually self-evident was not observed in practice and is therefore a major concern'. Other areas reported a lack of clarity and information about the aims of the different services, and consequently inappropriate assessment and allocation procedures.

More specifically, authorities mentioned the difficulties of discharging users from one sector to another, particularly from day hospital to day centre; the low level of input by health authorities and adult education departments to SSD day centres; the implications for the health authority of resource restraints on the local authority affecting SSD day care services; and the need for realistic funding of the voluntary sector by the local authority.

Some authorities had attempted to overcome such coordination difficulties, and had begun by reviewing, jointly or separately, day care services for elderly people in their area. We received 21 such reviews of day care, and other authorities claimed to be in the process of undertaking similar reviews. Although only a minority of authorities sent such information, this encouraging development shows that increased attention is being paid to this neglected area. Examples given below from the findings of day care reviews, the day care content of documents on services for elderly people, and from seminar participants, should prove of interest to other authorities considering joint planning of day care services.

Various approaches were taken to the coordination of services and the development of a continuum of day care. Authorities such as Norfolk and Coventry SSDs and Southampton and South West Hampshire HA recommended developing integrated plans for their areas. In Coventry it was proposed to establish 'a policy group of senior officers who would work in support of the JCC in establishing a joint day care strategy and would advise and receive information on implementation' from a development/implementation group of two officers with social services and nursing backgrounds and representation from the voluntary sector.

Other authorities proposed a more systematic range of levels of day care. Dorset SSD's strategy was 'to develop a continuum of day centres provided by a range of agencies to meet a variety of needs. To this end the development of smaller, local "social" centres for elderly people is being encouraged in collaboration with the voluntary sector, district council and health authorities'; the SSD day centre would be for specific rehabilitation and people at risk. Wiltshire SSD officers were examining, with the health authorities, distinctions between types of day care, and proposed a system whereby people could move from day hospital to 'primary' day care in SSD elderly people's homes, to 'secondary' community-based voluntary day care; the SSD also proposed to develop a third tier of 'mini day care' for three or four elderly people by a neighbouring 'hostess' in her own home.

More specific plans for liaison between health and local authorities were under consideration. A Waltham Forest SSD policy review stated that officers from the SSD and HA were 'developing an outline policy for day facility provision that distinguishes between health and local authority objectives and responsibilities'. Shropshire HA, while proposing increases in day hospital services, was also concerned not to overlap with SSD services in rural areas and was considering 'shared day care in conjunction with local authority social services'. Mid-Glamorgan SSD's working group stressed the importance of liaison with district councils over day centre use and of liaison more generally with other SSD and HA day service providers. Northamptonshire SSD's member review panel proposed 'that joint working should be consolidated and developed by the use of mainstream finance from the health and social services', and 'that officers of health and social services departments should consider the merits of the development of a joint day hospital/day care centre on an experimental basis'.

A number of SSDs were examining their liaison with voluntary sector day care providers. In Somerset, where the SSD has no full-time purpose-built day centres and uses, twice a week, two buildings shared with the health authority, the policy is to concentrate on voluntary 'mini day centres' to which people may move on after assessment or rehabilitation at the SSD-staffed centres. There are 48 such voluntary centres open once or twice a week in villages and linked with the SSD in each area. Hampshire SSD provided some day care services in collaboration with voluntary organisations but proposed to reduce its role from that of coordinator to an advisory and support function, and to fund day care coordinators in the voluntary sector.

Other proposals concerned liaison between the health and social services and voluntary sector. The Dorset SSD study group, for example, recommended that whereas day hospitals would provide for medical needs and elderly mentally infirm people, and the voluntary sector would offer social centres, the SSD should concentrate on providing care centres where 'there could be considerable scope for collaboration between health and social services personnel. Thus treatment programmes started in day hospitals could perhaps be continued possibly in a modified form in day centres'. A number of health authorities proposed that day hospitals should be strictly limited to assessment, rehabilitation and treatment, and that instead of increasing day hospital provision, day hospitals should have an input to more locally based day centres run by SSDs and voluntary organisations. Bromley HA's aim, for instance, was that 'the NHS should support day care provided by the local authority and voluntary associations through community health services, particularly district nursing and community physiotherapy services. The health authority can use its resources within hospital care for intensive rehabilitation of elderly people for community-based care'.

Coordination at operational level
Policy documents or operational procedures described the liaison arrangements which took place or were proposed between agencies or sectors of day care at an operational level. The more general observations listed the organisations with which day units did, or should, liaise. Bedfordshire SSD's social centres manual considered it important for centres to establish and maintain links with the home help organiser, SSD area office and fieldworkers, the health service, local schools and community organisations.

More detailed information concerned the main types of liaison arrangements: regular meetings, agreed procedures, joint training, and liaison officers. Darlington HA's liaison arrangements with the SSD, for instance, consisted of weekly multi-disciplinary meetings organised by consultant geriatricians, and fortnightly meetings on applications and allocations for part III places. Southern Derbyshire HA proposed to establish local resource groups which would meet regularly to discuss local resources and improve working arrangements; and Stockport SSD suggested more contact between social services officers and day centre organisers.

Where procedures are concerned, it is essential that those for assessment and allocation are clarified and accessible to all agencies so that appropriate placements or referrals can be made. A few policy documents took up this question. The report of South Tees HA's working group, *Our future too,* observed that there were very few operational procedures for services for elderly people and that such information was rarely shared with other agencies. The report recommended that, rather than relying on goodwill to sustain inter-agency relationships at operational level, all agencies should 'actively pursue the formulation of both written statements of objectives at a policy level, and a manual of systematised procedures, at an operational level' and that 'such statements be published in the form of a single document, to be shared as a common resource to all agencies'. Southern Derbyshire HA recognised that joint assessment was difficult in practice and recommended an approach which concentrated on very frail elderly people and on key decision points for each agency so that when such triggers were reached all local professionals would meet to devise a care plan.

Joint training was also mentioned by South Tees HA's working group which recommended formalising and building upon a joint-financed collaborative training scheme introduced in 1985 for SSD, NHS nursing and borough council housing staff on working with priority groups in the community. The nomination of an individual postholder as contact point or liaison officer was another method of fostering liaison. Some authorities had initiated posts specifically for inter-agency coordination. For example, South Tees HA recommended a joint-financed post for 'an individual whose principal responsibilities would be the coordination of inter-agency activities and the production of appropriate operational plans for the future'.

These examples of liaison arrangements illustrate the types of approach taken, although they cannot be considered representative as we did not ask specifically about such arrangements. More detailed papers were sent to CPA about particular joint projects which attempted to operationalise policies on coordination between agencies in offering community care and day care services to older people.

One type of joint project was the development of the primary health care centre into a wider community care and support centre. For example, the Lambeth Community Care Centre offered care from GPs, nurses, therapists, social workers, dentist, chiropodist, and support groups, and had a day unit for all ages. The Whittington Centre, Streatham, a health and support centre for the over 60s, had a similar range of professionals, a shop, hairdresser, volunteers, support groups, and home cooked lunches.

Other schemes, some similar to the Kent Community Care Project, coordinated the care of very dependent elderly people so that they could remain in their own homes. The Darlington community care project, run jointly by Darlington HA and Durham SSD, offered care by specially trained home care assistants who carried out domestic, caring and therapeutic tasks; individual care plans to provide 'intensive packages of home care support' were coordinated by the project team. The Gateshead SSD community care scheme, providing extra support for elderly people who would otherwise need residential care, was to be expanded to include a health component, starting with one group practice where a joint scheme would operate to provide additional medical and nursing care to prevent hospital admission.

A research and development project was being undertaken by the Open University and Policy Studies Institute in collaboration with Gloucester HA.[22] Care coordinators were attached to primary health care teams to gather and exchange information on local services and resources for elderly people, assess individual needs, arrange care packages linking statutory, voluntary and informal services, and monitor the effectiveness of the support given. Kirklees SSD planned two pilot schemes to offer a comprehensive locally based range of domiciliary, fieldwork, residential and day care services.

Some authorities had developed sites to provide integrated services for older people. Mid-Staffordshire HA proposed an 'Eldercentre' and combined day hospital and centre in Stone, on a centrally located site close to a GP surgery and housing for elderly people. The scheme consisted of ten elements, each of which could be developed, financed and managed separately, working to an overall framework: a community alarm scheme; community nursing; well elderly clinic; drop-in centre; sheltered housing; day hospital; respite beds; short-stay rehabilitation unit; beds for elderly severely mentally infirm people; and nursing home beds.

Derbyshire SSD and West Derbyshire district council's housing department had jointly developed the Underhall scheme, in coordination with North Derbyshire HA. Opened in 1985, it consisted of 40 flats with warden's house, eight-bed residential unit, meals on wheels kitchen, home help laundry, and communal rooms for 25 day care users, tenants, residents and visitors. At the centre needs were assessed and personal care plans developed. Hastings HA and East Sussex SSD had financed the Pinehill and Mount Denys development in community care for elderly people. The Pinehill resource centre offered seven days a week day and evening care, outreach services, assessment, clinical consultancy, support for carers, resources, advice and information, and a base for sessions by other organisations; and Mount Denys was a residential home for elderly mentally infirm people, jointly staffed by registered mental nurses and care officers.

The Minories in Newcastle was a design award winning complex with short-term residential care, day care, sheltered housing and a pop-in restaurant.[23] It was a joint local authority project between the SSD, housing department and city architects, and aimed to maintain frail elderly people in the community and support carers, targeting resources on the most vulnerable elderly people.

Turning to joint projects for day care in particular, there have been a number of articles and news items on developments. For example, *Social Work Today* reported on a new day centre in Richmond for elderly mentally ill people, jointly funded by the SSD and HA in liaison with the British Red Cross society.[24] Clayton described the Elms day centre, run by Age Concern

Witney, with joint finance, a grant from Oxfordshire SSD, other grants and locally raised funding.[25] Groups for elderly mentally infirm people were organised twice a week, one by an experienced volunteer, the other by a trained nurse, helped by volunteers on a rota basis; close links were maintained with community psychiatric nursing staff.

Several SSDs and HAs sent details of joint care projects. In Bolton, for example, a joint day facility for elderly people was proposed. A multi-disciplinary service would be offered and allocation of places would be jointly decided by an HA funded sister and an SSD funded coordinator. Greenwich joint planning group for elderly people proposed to establish a joint funded day centre 'for very physically frail elderly people who do not need further treatment and rehabilitation but are too frail to be cared for in the local authority's day clubs'. Barnsley SSD was developing day services for people with dementia in partnership with the HA; a 20-place centre was to open in 1988.

The Ringwood day care project for frail elderly people, financed by Salisbury HA and Hampshire SSD, had appointed a full-time coordinator to establish a day centre for up to eight people per day, five days a week, and a home care scheme offering day care five days a week in the homes of volunteers. Sefton SSD and Southport and Formby HA jointly funded a 35-place day unit for elderly mentally infirm people which was jointly operated by specialist staff for six days a week to 'provide an effective alternative to long-term residential or hospital admission'. In Walsall a new joint-financed, purpose-built day care centre for frail elderly people was opened in September 1987. The centre, attached to a sheltered housing unit, was staffed by SSD and HA workers.

Examples were also received of joint day care projects involving education services, voluntary agencies and other organisations. In North Tyneside there were plans to open a day centre for mentally infirm people at a school, with funding from the inner areas programme and joint finance; another joint-financed project would provide core staff for an Age Concern day centre for elderly mentally infirm people; and a day centre was planned in conjunction with Age Concern at a community high school. The Cotteridge project was planned by Birmingham SSD, South Birmingham HA and three churches. A church site was to be redeveloped into a place of worship and a meeting place for community groups including day centres for frail elderly people and for elderly mentally infirm people.

A further category of joint project comprises the day resource centre combining day care with other multi-disciplinary services and resources for elderly people in the community. Thompson described this model of service provision as a very positive development and suggested that the resource centre should undertake outreach work and develop the care activities of the locality, identifying and meeting needs for new services in cooperation with local agencies.[26] This model operated in Derbyshire, one of the pioneering areas for day resource centres, from whose SSD we received details of two schemes. The Lincote centre, Swadlincote, provided assessment and rehabilitation services for elderly people with severe problems who usually attended short-term and then received longer-term support organised by the centre. Lincote initiated the development of new resources in the community such as day care in sheltered housing, and a day centre run jointly with a church. The day resources Long Close project in Ripley offered a multi-purpose environment to be used by elderly people and their carers, the local community, and the centre's staff.

The Isle of Wight had two local authority residential/resource centres at opposite ends of the island. The centres provided day services and were supported by GPs, and by consultant geriatricians' domiciliary visits when necessary. It was claimed that the system reduced requests for hospital admission and day hospital places. A network of locally based day centres was planned.

Several authorities were considering the introduction of day resource centres. The first of the planned elderly persons support units in South Glamorgan was to open in the summer of 1988. The London borough of Sutton planned to build a day resource centre in 1988–89, to meet the needs of a wide range of elderly people, especially the very dependent. Wolverhampton SSD's proposal, supported by the HA, was to build day care units at homes for elderly people, to serve the local area and contribute to the network of resources. Stockport social services committee was also considering setting up an area resource centre to cater for the more dependent elderly people. The centre would offer shared interests and activities, care services including day care, and treatment services with input from the HA.

Devon SSD's strategic framework for planning included the community resource centre jointly run by the SSD and HA to provide a range of functions including day care; to coordinate and facilitate the development of services for local elderly people; to provide education and information for professionals and the community; and to offer support to carers. North East Essex HA's strategy recommended setting up neighbourhood resource centres in areas where elderly people were concentrated, to provide services and a focal point for local resources. The resource centre would be based in a local authority home for elderly people and be run by a multi-disciplinary team from the SSD and HA, which would design care packages, and provide day care, respite and residential care. The resource centre would be developed as a base for activities for elderly people and carers in the community and for residents of the home.

The role of informal carers
A common purpose of many of the joint projects, usually catering for the more dependent elderly people, was to offer support to carers in a flexible way. Although there has been little research into coordination between day care staff and carers, most previous studies indicate a need for more support for informal carers. Research on the experience of carers has shown that they rarely received all the community services which might have helped them, and that services offered were not always appropriate.[27,28]

Where relatives of day care users were concerned, studies found that in addition to the break provided by the day care service, carers needed additional help and support. Peace, for example, advocated 'more caring for the carers', and suggested that, 'Relatives can learn much from each other and from the staff about the management and aetiology of mental infirmity in old age. A day hospital may prove an ideal setting for a relatives support group'.[29] The East Anglia researchers recommended that, 'In general, links between home and centre should be improved and that the centre does more to support relatives, many of whom are themselves elderly and isolated'.[30]

One type of help which is often not accessible to elderly people and their carers is reliable information about services and facilities which might be available to them. A research project on information and support for elderly people in the inner city revealed that a majority of the respondents had information needs on topics such as housing and heating, finance, preventive health and social services, and social contacts.[31] A study of daughters who had cared for elderly mothers at home found that 'lack of information and knowledge about voluntary organisations and statutory services was one of the strongest themes running through the comments on sources of help'.[32]

Studies have also shown that professionals and workers in the various agencies are often inadequately informed about the range of services available to their clients, as Osborn pointed out in relation to day care: 'Many health and other professionals are ill-informed about day centre care and this may contribute to the underuse or abuse . . . and to the failure to involve the poorest or most isolated elderly people'.[33] Information is thus crucial to effective coordination between the various services and their elderly users or potential users, and carers.

Consumer studies on carers' and users' opinions of day care services are reported in chapter 8; a brief summary here of the findings will provide some background to current policy developments on supporting carers through day care services. Research has shown that many carers derived positive benefits from day care services for their elderly dependents. For example, Levin and her colleagues reported that supporters appreciated the free time, the break from coping with personal care and difficult behaviour and the opportunity in some cases to continue their paid work.[34] However, difficulties were identified. Day care was normally only available during the weekday whereas carers would often like a break at other times. Similarly the day unit opening hours and transport arrangements were frequently unsuitable for carers who worked outside the home. Perhaps the most difficult problem for carers was the unreliability of transport collection and return times.

The increasing recognition in recent years of the roles and difficulties of carers is reflected in the policies of statutory authorities on services for older people. Most of the strategic documents included support for carers as an integral part of helping dependent elderly people to live in the community. Some also stated their recognition of the importance of carers' knowledge of the elderly person and of their contribution to that person's care.

The importance of integrating formal and informal care was also accepted, and some authorities looked at ways in which different services and sectors could help meet the carer's needs. South Tyneside HA's review of services, for example, included among practical ways of helping carers 'respite and holiday care, day care, a night sitting service, advice and help on dealing with incontinence'. Crossroads care attendant schemes and voluntary day sitting services were cited by several authorities as examples of practical help for carers.

For relatives of day care users, some strategic documents aimed to make the service more widely available and more flexible. Sefton SSD's working party, for example, identified attributes that day care provision should have, including availability seven days a week from early morning until evening, and wide publicity. Several day hospitals sent us copies of attractive leaflets about the service they provided.

Another aspect of policy concerned contacts between day unit staff and carers, with an emphasis on building good relationships, as given in Bedfordshire SSD's social centres manual. In this way, carers could contribute to the day service's work through their knowledge of the elderly person and also perhaps more actively as volunteers, and day unit staff could offer support and advice to the people caring for their clients at home. This applied particularly to carers of elderly mentally infirm people for whom the support of professionals such as community psychiatric nurses could be very helpful. Relatives' support groups were suggested as a practical way of promoting support for carers.

Providing information for carers on the different services available was the stated policy of several authorities. The methods of imparting such information varied. Dorset SSD planned 'to promote and support a range of information points in the community from which elderly people and their carers can seek appropriate advice and information'. Greenwich HA's joint planning group proposed a 'resource centre to be run by Age

Concern providing information on all services to elderly people', and 'further exploration of how information and advice can be made available to carers on a 24-hour basis'. Some authorities advocated using the day care unit as a base for information and advice for elderly people and carers. For example, Gateshead HA's strategic plan included a new day hospital which would involve voluntary organisations, carers and families and which 'could become a focal point for coordinating information and advice, as well as services for the elderly'.

A number of authorities sent to CPA examples of locally prepared leaflets or booklets on services for elderly people. Southern Derbyshire HA's joint planning group considered that one role of their proposed local resource groups would be to publish guides to services available and that 'preparation of such guides can be a valuable exercise'. This is consistent with the findings of the above-mentioned study on information for older people which advocated a coordinated local approach to collating and updating information on a range of topics.[35]

Types and levels of coordination and cooperation
The various sources used by this study reiterated the need for improved coordination and cooperation at policy and operational levels between the relevant services and between service providers and their users and carers. The main types and levels of coordination are summarised below.

1. Community care and day care

Policy level
Joint planning.
Joint review of policy/service provision.
Jointly agreed procedures.
Communication/information.

Operational level
Joint assessment.
Key workers.
Care packages.
Integrated local services.
Communication/information.

2. Sectors of day care

Policy level
Joint meetings on policy.
Joint planning of provision for locality.
Joint review of policy/provision.
Clarification of roles for each type of service.
Policy on joint funding/grant aid.

Operational level
Referrals/discharge between sectors.
Liaison meetings between and within sectors.
Agreed operational procedures.
Liaison officers.
Input to other services.
Joint training.
Joint project and shared resources.

3. Providers and carers

Policy level
Policy on support for carers.
Identification of needs of carers.
Meeting needs of carers of day care users.
Information for elderly people, carers and workers.

Operational level
Communication between day unit staff and carers.
Involvement of carers as volunteers.
Carers' support groups.
Information for carers and workers.

REFERENCES
1. A. Norton, B. Stoten and H. Taylor, *Councils of care: planning a local government strategy for older people*, Centre for Policy on Ageing, London, 1986
2. R. Bowl, H. Taylor, M. Taylor and N. Thomas, *Day care for the elderly in Birmingham*, University of Birmingham Social Services Unit, Birmingham, 1978
3. A. Osborn, *Day care for older people in day centres*, Age Concern Scotland, Edinburgh, 1985, p 6
4. S.M. Peace, *Caring from day to day*, MIND, London, 1980
5. Bowl *et al, Day care for the elderly*
6. J. Carter, *Day services for adults—somewhere to go*, George Allen and

Unwin, London, 1981

7. Audit Commission, *Managing social services for the elderly more effectively*, HMSO, London, 1985, p 49

8. R. Griffiths, *Community care: agenda for action*, HMSO, London, 1988

9. Bowl *et al, Day care for the elderly*, para 12.6

10. E.M. Goldberg and N. Connelly, *The effectiveness of social care for the elderly*, Policy Studies Institute, London, 1982

11. M. Bayley, P. Parker, R. Seyd and A. Tennant, *Practising community care—developing locally based practice*, University of Sheffield Joint Unit for Social Services Research and *Community Care*, 1987

12. J.E. Tibbitt, Day care—a 'good thing'? in G. Horobin (ed), *Why day care?*, Research highlights in social work 14, Jessica Kingsley, London, 1987

13. Audit Commission, *Making a reality of community care*, HMSO, London, 1986

14. Griffiths, *Community care*

15. D.J. Hunter and K. Judge, *Griffiths and community care: meeting the challenge*, King's Fund Institute, London, 1988

16. Griffiths, *Community care*

17. Griffiths, *Community care*, p vii, para 24

18. Peace, *Caring from day to day*

19. Bowl *et al, Day care for the elderly*, para 12.8

20. Bowl *et al, Day care for the elderly*, para 12.8

21. G. Fennell, A.R. Emerson, M. Sidell and A. Hague, *Day centres for the elderly in East Anglia*, University of East Anglia School of Economic and Social Studies, Norwich, 1981

22. See project papers, T. Dant, M. Carley, B. Gearing and M. Johnson, *Care of elderly people at home: a research and development project in collaboration with Gloucester HA*, Open University and Policy Studies Institute, Milton Keynes and London, 1987

23. G. Rothapel, Pride of Newcastle, *Community Care*, 710, 1988, 26–27

24. Joint funding for new day centre, *Social Work Today*, 18, 22, 1987, 17

25. P. Clayton, Never too old to lend a hand, *Health Services Journal*, 97, 5044, 395

26. K. Thompson, A climate of care, *Social Services Insight*, 2, 29, 1987, 15–17

27. J. Lewis and B. Meredith, *Daughters who care: daughters caring for mothers at home*, Routledge, London and New York, 1988

28. E. Levin, I. Sinclair and P. Gorbach, *The supporters of confused elderly persons at home*, National Institute for Social Work research unit, London, 1983

29. Peace, *Caring from day to day*, p 31

30. Fennell *et al, Day centres for the elderly*, p 204

31. S. Tester and B. Meredith, *Ill-informed? A study of information and support for elderly people in the inner city*, Policy Studies Institute, London, 1987

32. Lewis and Meredith, *Daughters who care*, p 98

33. Osborn, *Day care for older people*, p 4

34. Levin *et al, The supporters of confused elderly persons*

35. Tester and Meredith, *Ill-informed?*

7 Transport and developments

Transport is almost invariably seen as one of the most problematic issues concerning day care services. Most responses to CPA's trawl of HAs and SSDs described transport services in terms of a problem which was 'insoluble', 'intractable', the 'Achilles heel' of the day care service. Some gave details of existing transport services, the difficulties entailed, and the policies and practices adopted or planned to reduce the problems of transporting users to day units.

Current practice in transport provision
A minority of day units, mainly non-statutory ones, owned and ran their own transport, sometimes using vehicles funded by Help the Aged. Other transport services, however, were administered centrally, individual day units liaising with the transport service to arrange journeys for users. The availability of transport from these services placed constraints on the numbers of users who could attend day units.

Day hospitals had perhaps more difficulties over transport than other types of unit. Their transport was usually provided by the ambulance service for the area, which was also responsible for emergency services and non-emergency journeys to outpatients' departments. The needs of day hospital patients did not always receive priority from these services, particularly when emergencies, bad weather or staff illness caused unexpected delays. Catchment areas for day hospitals sometimes overlapped with ambulance service areas so that a day hospital had to liaise with two or more ambulance services. In some areas, a 'dedicated' ambulance and staff were provided by the ambulance service for a particular day hospital. This could, however, mean that different ambulances were collecting people from the same area for different day hospitals. Another system was zoning, whereby patients from the same area were taken to the same day hospital on specific days. But this might limit the number of days a patient could attend each week, and was not always practicable when individual needs were met by different day hospitals.

Similar difficulties were experienced when local authorities ran transport services which were used by those attending day centres and day care in residential homes. Where there were competing needs for transport of, say, physically handicapped children or mentally handicapped adults, the elderly day centre users did not always receive priority. The numbers of clients taken each day to day centres was limited by the transport resources available, and, where these resources were fully committed, emergencies such as staff absences led to cancellations or delays.

Some SSDs issued guidance to individual day units on liaising with centrally managed transport services. For example, Bedfordshire SSD's social centres manual stipulated that the officer-in-charge should compile transport lists in cooperation with the transport manager; that lists should be revised frequently; and that transport runs should be as short as possible.

Criteria for allocation of transport were rarely mentioned by authorities but several SSDs stated that transport was only provided for people who needed it and had no other means of travelling to the centre. In some cases, relatives were expected to provide transport. Those who received transport services were, not surprisingly, the most dependent elderly people with physical and/or mental disabilities. Varying proportions of these users were unable to walk and needed a vehicle with a tail-lift, or two people to lift them into an ambulance. Others could walk a short distance with the help of a walking frame or one person. Where users were mentally infirm an escort was required so that the drivers did not have to leave passengers unattended. Thus, ambulances transporting dependent elderly people to day units often needed two crew members.

The types of vehicle used by transport services had implications for the numbers and types of elderly people who could be taken to day care units. Three types of vehicle were identified as being used for day care services in the Medway district: 'stretcher cars', ambulances with seats lengthwise along the sides which were also used for emergencies; 'sitting cars', ambulances with forward-facing seats, with or without a tail-lift; and minibuses, some with tail-lifts.[1] Of the six units studied two used ambulances run by the Kent ambulance service, three ran their own ambulances and one had its own minibus.

For day hospital transport, Brocklehurst and Tucker thought that the ideal vehicle 'should have forward-facing, chair-type seats, good visibility through the windows and easy communication between the driver and his passengers. It should be warm and have a tail-lift'.[2] Very few authorities gave details, in response to CPA's trawl, of the type of vehicle used for day hospitals. A study for Gloucester HA showed that most of the 100 patients travelling daily to day hospitals for elderly people used the hospital transport service; the range of vehicles used included 'single-staffed tail-lift vehicles, single-staffed sitting case vehicles, dual-staffed sitting case vehicles, the hospital car service and, in one case, a bus provided by a private coach company'.[3]

The Gloucester survey found that average journey times to day hospitals were 40 minutes in the morning and 33 minutes in the afternoon, with a range from a few minutes to just over 2½ hours (in one case). Patients arrived between 9.10 a.m. and 11.15 a.m. and left between 3.00 p.m. and 5.05 p.m; most had arrived by 10.15 a.m. and had left before 4.00 p.m. The most problematic journeys to day units in Medway were to the day hospital; for 21% of patients the journey took over one hour. Shorter journey times were, however, reported for units with their own ambulances.

Examples of day centre transport provided by SSDs showed that SSD units were often served by local authority ambulances each making two runs to and from a centre. A review of day care services by Liverpool SSD found that, of 140 people interviewed, 120 travelled to day centres by tail-lift ambulance, 13 made their own way and seven went by car or were taken by a relative. A Norfolk SSD study group report on services to elderly people showed that many centres relied on volunteer drivers using their own cars, although special minibuses were used for very disabled people; the report stressed the need for a balance and integration between these forms of transport.

Many of the Norfolk day centres in rural areas were run by voluntary organisations. A survey of voluntary day centres in Croydon provided examples of transport to such centres in urban areas. Four of the ten centres had their own minibus, six had volunteer drivers with their own cars, three used SSD vehicles and six used taxis or hired cars. Of the 438 client days per week, 205 people used SSD vehicles, 144 used the centre's own minibus, 61 used voluntary drivers, 26 travelled by taxi and two by other methods. The expenses of voluntary drivers were reimbursed by the local authority which also paid a mileage allowance to centres using their own minibus.

Several commentators and HA and SSD documents stressed the important role played by crews of various types of transport to day care units since, as the East Anglia report showed, 'Drivers and escorts are likely to be sensitive to users' needs and act as a vital link between home and centre'.[4] The Medway report, however, pointed out that this was more likely to occur where the same crew regularly accompanied the same passengers than when county ambulance services were used, since 'where vehicles are likely to make different journeys each day, picking up different patients as the computer dictates, it is hard for staff to get to know the people whom they transport'.[5]

Bedfordshire SSD's social centres manual suggested that the journey 'should be an enjoyable extension to the client day' and stated that, 'The officer-in-charge must ensure an effective link between transport drivers and centre staff. The driver will inevitably have knowledge of the client which will be of value in helping that client whilst in the centre (and vice versa)'. Gwynedd SSD's day care manual advised that if transport staff were likely to have to enter the client's home, the driver should be accompanied by an assistant supervisor. Other authorities mentioned the difficulties of having vehicles with only one crew member, particularly where elderly mentally ill clients were concerned.

This brief overview of existing transport services has already touched on some of the logistical difficulties of transporting a fluctuating number of elderly people from geographically dispersed rural areas or congested towns to several different day units at set times in the morning and afternoon. We shall now examine, in some detail, the main problems reported by commentators and service providers.

Problems in transport provision

Non-availability of transport for day care units for older people was a general difficulty, reported particularly by SSDs. This was partly due to the high costs of transport and a basic shortage of transport resources, but also to the lower priority accorded to elderly day care users by general transport services. Brocklehurst and Tucker, for example, commented that, 'Many drivers thought the day hospital was more of a social club than a treatment centre. This may be why the ambulance service gives a low priority to day hospital care'.[6] Geographical variations in transport availability also meant limited access to day care services for elderly people in certain areas.

A related difficulty was that transport was only available at certain times of the day. Cumbria SSD's working party on day care for elderly people, for example, reported that, 'Transport problems in many areas restrict day care to the period 10.30 a.m. to 3.30 p.m., hardly more than a lunch club', and explained this by the use of general ambulance services and of SSD minibuses which transported adult mentally handicapped people earlier and later in the day. The need to fit users in with transport times reduced the flexibility of day care services so that they were often unable to provide the services at the times most suitable for users and carers.

Even when transport was available it was not necessarily of the right type or size. The shortage of tail-lift ambulances was a particular problem for those trying to arrange day care services for wheelchair users. The extent to which day hospitals could discharge disabled patients to day centres was also limited if these centres were unable to provide transport for them. Staffing the vehicles which were available constituted a further difficulty in providing back-up crews to cover staff absences, and in recruiting and retaining volunteer drivers for non-statutory minibuses and cars.

The various implications of these transport shortages included limited access to day care places for those most likely to need them, the more disabled and housebound elderly people. Tower Hamlets SSD's working party report on services and policy for elderly people, for example, pointed out that, 'Allocation of places depends to a large extent on availability of transport. The result is that places are not necessarily allocated according to need, and those who can make their own way to the centres on the whole attend more frequently than those who come by L. B. Tower Hamlets coach'. Another effect was that available places were not used, as, for example, in Greenwich health district where transport difficulties meant that only one-half of the 50 places in each of the two day hospitals were regularly taken up.

Authorities attempting to expand day care services or change their policies also found transport shortages an obstacle. Lewisham SSD, where present day care users were fairly active, was considering the possibility of targeting resources on the more dependent people, but the extent to which the proportion of dependent people could be increased was limited by the current transport resources. Arranging transport was also a difficulty for authorities wishing to develop evening and weekend day care services.

A cautionary note was, however, added by Coventry HA and SSD where a joint working party on day care had found a widespread belief by HA and SSD staff that shortage of transport for day care services was a major problem. This belief was, in fact, erroneous but its effect had been to inhibit referrals. The study showed that, although the ambulance service was fully committed, there was spare capacity in the SSD transport service.

Of the problems arising from the transport services actually provided, long journeys in terms of both distance and time were a frequent complaint. Long distances were often inevitable in rural areas especially for ambulance passengers. This could affect take-up of services. For example, South East Kent HA reported that people living more than ten miles from the day hospital were less likely to attend, and that patients living within four or five miles were more likely to use the service than those living five to ten miles away. The Medway report identified factors which affected the length of the journey, including 'the distance between the client's home and the centre; the number of other people who have to be picked up and the location of their homes; the number of putting down points and the distance between them; the skill with which routes are planned'.[7]

Long journey times of one hour or more were perceived as a problem by writers and service providers. Buckinghamshire and Norfolk SSDs, for instance, mentioned the difficulties of long journey times in rural areas. Fennell and his colleagues, however, pointed out that congestion in towns was just as likely to cause long journey times.[8] The limited hours of transport availability mentioned above meant that, in urban areas, journeys to and from day care units often coincided with at least part of the morning and afternoon rush hour traffic. Long journey times in the Medway district resulted from the wide catchment area, the failure to implement zoning, the fact that ambulance staff were not familiar with individuals' circumstances, and the complicated journeys to different hospitals and clinics.[9]

Day care providers and staff were concerned about long journey times partly because of the possible discomfort of elderly people with incontinence or painful conditions. A paper from a Brighton HA day hospital observed that many patients did not take their diuretics because of the long journey. Travel sickness was another factor. A survey of 172 patients, all except six of whom travelled by ambulance to a geriatric day hospital, showed that 19% had complained of travel sickness.[10] Fear of travel sickness had potentially or actually deterred attendance at some time by seven patients. The researchers suggested that emergency vehicles were unsuitable for this type of transport and that sickness would be less likely in vehicles with forward-facing seats and good vision for passengers. They also successfully treated patients for travel sickness and recommended that, since they had found an association between present and previous sickness, 'all patients be specifically questioned about prior travel sickness with a view to prescribing prophylactic therapy in selected patients'.[11]

Despite the concerns of staff and some transport users, a number of surveys and data collected for the present study have shown that some users found the long journey an enjoyable part of their day out and had no complaints about it.

Unpredictability of transport services was perceived by carers, users, staff and commentators as a more serious problem than long journeys. For users and carers, uncertainty about collection and return times could mean lengthy waits which were very frustrating and disturbed daily routines. The East Anglia study concluded that, 'Utmost regularity and predictability of pick-up/drop-off time are of vital importance in relieving relatives and maintaining the morale of the user'.[12] Day care staff experienced difficulties when users arrived late through transport delays as this disrupted activities and programmes.

The most frequent explanation for the unreliability of transport was staff absence through annual or sickness leave especially when this was unexpected. A report on discussions of Southwark day centre social workers observed that day centres for elderly people were adversely affected by departmental policies which gave priority to other groups when cancellation of transport was necessary. As mentioned earlier, unpredictability also resulted from the diversion of ambulances to emergency duties.

One of the most damaging effects of the limited hours of availability of transport, long journeys and unpredictable schedules was the reduction in time spent by users at the day unit. Day care service providers complained about late arrivals which meant that activities or treatment had to start late in the morning or be interrupted. Similarly, users often had to be prepared for their journey home by about 3.00 p.m. even though the transport might not arrive until much later; this caused restlessness and distraction from the programme of activities. Writers and service providers urged that transport schedules should not be allowed to affect the content of the day care service in this way. For example, a review of services by Liverpool SSD found that drivers had arrived early and tried to hurry users away from the day centre. The review concluded that, 'Officers-in-charge should take a firm stand against this practice and ensure, wherever possible, that elderly people arrive at the day centre no later than 10.30 a.m. and leave no earlier than 3.30 p.m. Each client should thus have a minimum of five hours day care.'

There was widespread consensus that the implications of transport problems impeded the successful running of day care programmes and constituted obstacles to the development of services. In attempting to mitigate the effects of transport difficulties, two main approaches were taken. First, efforts were made to improve the transport services; and second, attempts were made to circumvent the problems by reducing the need for transport.

Improving transport services
Researchers and service providers have shown that unavailability of transport resulting from under-resourcing or inefficient use of transport services has the further effect of underuse of scarce day unit resources. Alison Norman described this as 'a classic example of false economy'.[13] The 1985 Audit Commission report, which found day care transport costs much higher than necessary, gave examples of methods used in the study areas to reduce transport costs and increase availability of transport, such as using day centre transport for lunch clubs, using taxi services or volunteers, and sharing transport.[14] Some authorities responding to CPA's trawl cited similar methods while others detailed their plans for an increase in transport funding or resources.

A paper for Humberside SSD reported underuse of day care places, recommended the purchase of additional vehicles, and asked that consideration be given to appointing extra full-time drivers and part-time escorts. The Southwark centre social workers' report pointed out that as the proportion of dependent day centre users was increasing from 50% to 60%, the number of transport places would have to be increased. In Wiltshire SSD officers were considering the use of Help the Aged funding to provide additional minibuses for community-based day centres.

Other authorities stressed the importance of securing an adequate budget for transport. Cumbria SSD's working party, for example, recommended that 'adequate finance for transport is included for all day centres. However, each district should have one budget for transport to enable flexibility of use'. Southampton and South West Hampshire HA's priorities for joint day care development included 'coordination of transport arrangements so that each centre can run at maximum occupancy'.

Coordination, both between different transport services and between these services and individual units, was frequently cited as a method of improving transport efficiency. The ideal, mentioned by several authorities, was a coordinated transport system for an area, involving all the relevant agencies, client groups and types of venue. Since this would be administratively very complex, most authorities set themselves more limited and more easily attainable objectives.

The first task was to identify transport needs and resources in an area. An important part of identifying needs was to review existing passenger lists. Norman pointed out that this should be done regularly and could mean withdrawing transport services from people who no longer needed them.[15] Norfolk SSD's review of the county's transport needs identified a shortfall of about 12% of the total day care days required by clients, and recommended providing more day care transport by increasing the numbers of transport staff and vehicles, and changing the type of vehicle used. The Coventry joint working party concluded that a pilot action project on the coordination of statutory and voluntary transport should be initiated.

The idea of 'transport brokerage' for an area was also considered. This would require a coordinating group or officer to devise an overall policy and to organise the best use of transport resources to meet various identified transport needs in the area. One of Stockport SSD's proposals for community-based day centres was 'specialist coordinators employed for each area who would allocate the vehicles to the clubs etc. and would be available for liaison with day centre organisers to ensure economic use of vehicles and sufficient cover for all emergencies'.

More specific administrative approaches to coordination included sharing vehicles between two or more day care services. Peace, for example, suggested the sharing of transport by social services and voluntary organisations providing social day care in an area.[16] Coventry's joint working party concluded that the relevant authorities should consider making SSD vehicles available for day hospital transport. A joint consultative paper for Plymouth HA and Devon SSD considered that whereas a fully coordinated system was potentially 'an administrative nightmare', it would be advisable to discover obvious overlaps and to prevent their happening by linking different services.

Zoning was one of the more frequently mentioned measures to improve coordination of transport services and reduce journey times. This system, whereby users from the same area were brought to the day unit on the same day, had been successfully adopted in Barnsley HA district, where it had led to shorter journeys and longer stays at the day hospital. It had also meant reorganisation of nurses' working hours so that the unit was staffed for earlier arrivals and later departures.

Turning to the question of whether transport should be specific to day units, the use of general transport services was considered inappropriate for day unit users by researchers and policy makers. Brocklehurst and Tucker, for example, concluded, 'Now that the geriatric day hospital is firmly established as a regular part of the NHS, the time has certainly been reached when it requires its own separate and suitable transport system'.[17] Peace made similar recommendations for psychogeriatric day hospitals, and Fennell and his colleagues also recommended that transport with drivers and escorts serve particular local authority day centres.[18,19]

For day hospitals, transport specific to the unit was provided in some districts by ambulances and crews from local ambulance services being 'dedicated' to particular day hospitals. Health authorities such as North Derbyshire, North Bedfordshire and South Manchester were considering such systems. The Medway report discussed the possibility of a group of four dedicated ambulances serving the day hospital and another unit in order to increase efficiency and allow drivers and escorts to take the same users each week.[20] Similarly, a working party report for Tower Hamlets SSD recommended allocating each day centre its own transport and employing escorts as part of the day centre staff. Newcastle upon Tyne SSD was considering decentralisation of transport to day centres, a system already in operation at one centre.

One of the disadvantages of specific vehicles and staff for day units was that they might not be used efficiently in the middle of the day. Several authorities, however, suggested that drivers and escorts be employed in the day unit as caretakers, handypersons or care assistants when the transport was not in use. Having vehicles available also increased the possibility of taking users on outings, shopping trips and to other venues such as hairdressers, chiropodists or clinics.

Another approach was to reappraise the times at which journeys were made and to introduce more flexible opening hours for day units. The Medway report, for example, considered offering a 'flexi-day', with two groups of patients each spending five hours at the day hospital, one from 9.30 a.m. to 2.30 p.m., the other from 11.30 a.m. to 4.30 p.m., with transport runs starting at 8.30 a.m., 10.30 a.m., 2.30 p.m. and 4.30 p.m.[21] The Plymouth joint consultative paper, discussing transport services for elderly people, questioned the need for travel to day centres at peak commuter times and suggested opening day centres from late morning to early evening, particularly for elderly confused people who needed more help in the later part of the day.

More specific administrative solutions were suggested by authorities with problems arising from the use of general transport services. The Southwark centre social workers' report proposed that the centres which had priority could take a small share of cancellations so that the whole burden did not fall on elderly users. In Cumbria, where elderly day centre users had to fit in with transport runs to centres for mentally handicapped adults, it was suggested that some elderly people could be transported before and after the other groups. Stockport SSD proposed that minibuses should only be used to transport clients and not for other purposes such as delivering aids to people with disabilities.

Different sources of transport to day units were also used or being considered as ways of easing transport difficulties. These were usually to be combined with existing services, to supplement rather than replace them. The use of volunteer car services and taxis was considered, for example in the Medway report, for the 60% of users whom the study found able to travel by car, combined with ambulance services for the 40% who needed them.[22] The report perceived the advantages of this system to be shorter journeys and friendly relationships between drivers and passengers, but warned of the disadvantages of increased administrative work involved in recruiting drivers and arranging journeys. Cumbria SSD's working party suggested using the social work car service and a taxi service rather than relying on the minibus transport which gave priority to other groups. The Plymouth joint consultative paper's suggestions for alternative forms of transport for those not needing ambulance services included the hospital car service, volunteer escorts to help people travel to day centres on public transport, and use of the Citybus flexible routed minibus service.

The wider question of transport services for older people also received attention in research publications and policy documents. People who could not use public transport were likely to find that the only transport which might be offered to them was for special venues such as day hospitals or day centres. A study of transport in London for people with disabilities found that ambulance service transport was only for health-related needs and that borough transport provision mainly consisted of transport to day centres.[23] Transport services for disabled older people to the facilities used by the general population might be more acceptable and meet their needs for company more appropriately than transport to a day centre.

A CPA study of voluntary transport services, however, found that older people with mobility problems needed some encouragement to use more general facilities because it was more difficult for them to be accepted at such venues than at day centres.[24] Long-term changes in attitudes towards people with disabilities would be needed to remedy this situation. The study, however, showed that people using a voluntary car service initially for transport to essential services had gradually been encouraged to use it for more social purposes.[25]

Voluntary transport services have also met needs both for individual transport and for travel to group facilities such as day care units. These services differ between rural and urban areas, as pointed out in the CPA report.[26] In rural areas voluntary transport schemes compensate for poor public transport and are open to the general public, whereas in urban areas they are only for people who cannot use public transport and for voluntary agencies' transport needs. The GLAD report found that minibuses used by community transport schemes for all types of need, including transport to day units, were often unsuitable for disabled people, particularly those in wheelchairs.[27] Further, these schemes met group rather than individual needs; dial-a-ride services and the taxi card scheme were being developed in many parts of London to serve individual transport needs. There could be scope for developing the use of community transport and dial-a-ride services for transport to day care units, but at present such services tend to be oversubscribed in many areas.

Reducing the need for transport

Transport problems were alleviated in some locations by bringing day care services closer to users in various ways so that long-distance journeys from people's homes were unnecessary. Two main approaches used were to introduce travelling or mobile services, and to localise day care services.

Travelling and mobile services

Travelling day hospitals were pioneered in the 1970s. St James' Hospital, Portsmouth, initiated a psychogeriatric travelling day hospital in 1982 to reduce transport costs, provide local day hospital care, and involve local agencies in this care.[28] The travelling day hospital catered for patients with functional mental illnesses, such as depression, who required some supervision and support but did not need in-patient or day hospital care. The day hospital staff travelled to four different centres, each open one day a week, taking about 15 patients a day. The fifth day was spent on administration, meetings, liaison with local agencies, and home visits. Patients were brought by minibus and travel times were short, allowing more time to be spent on treatment than in traditional day hospitals. Another advantage was the greater willingness of patients to attend a service which they saw as less stigmatising than normal day hospitals.[29]

Southampton and South West Hampshire HA's joint day care development included a travelling day hospital called 'Inroads', which visited five different sites, in day centres and sheltered housing schemes, each week, taking a maximum of 15 patients a day. The patients were mostly over 65 and suffered from functional or organic mental illnesses. The travelling day hospital's purpose was 'to provide a local day hospital service for referred psychogeriatric patients'. The service had its own transport and all staff were responsible for collecting, driving and returning it. An advantage of this staff involvement in transporting patients was the opportunity provided for staff to persuade reluctant patients to attend, thus ensuring high attendance rates. The budget for this travelling service was £48,000 per annum. The same HA was also considering the possibilities of introducing a travelling day hospital service within a day centre, and a once a week travelling service for isolated rural areas.

York HA had recently established a 10–15 place travelling day hospital. Other health authorities, including the Isle of Wight, were currently considering such initiatives. The experience of the early travelling day hospitals showed that this was a useful way of extending services to different geographical areas, providing decentralised, less stigmatising services and reducing transport costs and journey times.

Travelling or mobile day centres were also proposed. In Peterborough a joint-finance project to establish a mobile day centre was to be implemented. This would be held in outlying areas using venues such as communal facilities in sheltered housing schemes once or twice a week. County SSDs such as Lincolnshire, and Hereford and Worcester, were also examining the feasibility of mobile day centres in rural areas. North Derbyshire HA was considering mobile day centres/resource centres, particularly for isolated areas in West Derbyshire and the High Peak, either with staff visiting existing health clinics, or by using converted trailers to carry staff and equipment. The services would be set up in cooperation with local communities and might be jointly financed. In addition to day centre/hospital services with nurses, social workers and therapists, it would be possible to offer audiology technicians, aids and wheelchair technicians and chiropody or foot care services. The HA allocated £200,000 in 1987–88 to promote this development.

Other authorities used, or were considering, a mobile unit which could be towed to different venues. One example was the mobile day centre in Beverley, Humberside, which began in June 1985.[30] The mobile day unit, equipped for disabled users, was towed by an SSD minibus to a different village each weekday, and parked for example in village school grounds so that mains services could be used. The bus collected up to 12 users, with an average age in the mid-eighties, and brought them to the unit. The service had a full-time supervisor and full-time driver/ attendant, and volunteers in each village, one of whom helped at each session.

The mobile unit catered for the most dependent elderly people; criteria for attendance were handicap or infirmity, need for support to remain in the community, social isolation, dependence on carers, and need for rehabilitation. The advantages of the mobile day centre included accessibility of day care to a larger population, suitability for disabled users as the bus and unit were purpose-adapted, and savings on equipment and adaptations to village halls. The users reacted very positively to the service. Although the scheme had high initial capital costs, it was cost-effective and provided an increased day care service to those who needed it most.

In Hampshire, Help the Aged's jubilee appeal was fundraising for a mobile day centre to be run in cooperation with the SSD and Age Concern, with a paid coordinator and volunteers. This scheme would have a trailer which could be bolted on to use the mains services of a village hall where the day centre activities would be carried out. The trailer would provide specialised facilities and equipment including toilets, bathing, hairdressing and foot care services. The vehicle which towed the trailer would also collect users from their homes. When not in use for the mobile day centre, the trailer could be used at other sites to provide toilet facilities and information for people with disabilities.

Localised services
Transport problems have reduced the effectiveness of providing centralised day care services to which users are transported some distance from their homes. Consequently, several authorities have begun to re-examine the location of day care services and to suggest changing to more localised services. Authorities tended now to propose smaller day centres, as evenly distributed as possible throughout the area, using existing community facilities and sharing buildings with other users. The buildings would not be purpose-built as day centres, but some authorities stipulated that they should be accessible to wheelchair users and ideally have bathing facilities and toilets suitable for disabled people.

Localisation of day care services was especially appropriate to rural areas. Humberside SSD had developed rural day centres in parts of the county not covered by purpose-built centres. Chester HA reported that small rural day centres had been set up by local people with help from the SSD. Norfolk SSD's study group report recommended identifying suitable buildings in rural areas without day care services and staffing day centres in these buildings with peripatetic day care teams, which would visit centres on different days.

Mini day centres in rural and urban areas not served by existing centres had been established, for example in Cumbria, mostly run by voluntary groups once or twice a week. Cambridgeshire SSD was turning to the model of a small day centre for a small population, and seeking to locate such centres in housing schemes for elderly people, schools, residential homes and so forth. Similar priorities were set by Southampton and South West Hampshire's joint day care development group. Health authorities also sought to localise day care services. For example, Scunthorpe HA proposed to locate expansion of day hospital places not in the general hospital which had a wide catchment area, but in a small district to provide a service for local elderly residents.

Another aspect of localisation of services is the provision of resource centres and integrated services as described in chapter 6. In Salford HA it was proposed in the long term to provide throughout the district localised complexes offering long-stay, respite and day care for local people. Southern Derbyshire HA also produced resource centres in each locality based on existing buildings such as clinics or residential homes, to offer a combination of services including flexible day care to meet the needs of individuals.

Day care in private homes could also offer a more localised form of care. Wiltshire SSD officers envisaged the development of this type of 'hostessing' as third tier day care. In Hampshire the Ringwood pilot home care scheme provided a day care service for geographically isolated clients for whom it was impracticable to provide transport. 'Day carers' were recruited to take elderly people into their own homes for the day. This system has been used successfully by the Kent Community Care Scheme[31], and the Gateshead Community Care Scheme[32], to provide local day care for vulnerable or mentally infirm elderly people who could not cope with a long journey or a whole day in a busy centre.

One of the problems with providing localised day care of various types is that users will only meet a small group of other elderly people and may not find a compatible companion among them, although reducing loneliness through social contacts is often a stated aim of day care services. Further, in small groups it is important that all participants relate well to each other. Those who are eccentric or withdrawn or have behaviour difficulties, and thus have urgent needs for day care services, may be excluded as unacceptable to the rest of the group. Another difficulty is that it may be expensive to resource a smaller number of local venues rather than one larger centre. If voluntary agencies or volunteers are involved there are often difficulties in securing long-term funding and in recruiting volunteers.

These disadvantages, however, may be outweighed by the considerable advantages of reduced transport problems and shorter journeys, and the increased accessibility of day care services to people in districts previously not served by them, particularly in rural areas. Rural day centres organised by voluntary groups with support from statutory agencies were considered a good example of inter-agency coordination. They were generally perceived to be good value for money. Localised provision facilitated the involvement of the local community as volunteers, and served as a type of outreach opportunity for statutory agencies to work in localities some distance away from their main offices and centralised services.

Types of good practice
Day care transport needs are determined by the type of area and location of day care services and users within the area. It would be difficult to devise an ideal transport system suitable for all areas. We have, however, described some of the methods advocated by commentators and used or proposed by statutory and voluntary agencies in rural and urban areas of England and Wales. The types of solution to transport problems suggested on the basis of the findings of this study are summarised below.

1. Resources and cost-effectiveness
Exploration of all sources of funding, for example joint finance, Help the Aged.
Adequate number of vehicles of appropriate type and size.
Adequate number of drivers and escorts, and arrangements for emergency cover.

Correct number of transport places for people with assessed needs.
Adequate number of day unit staff to cover earlier arrivals and later departures of transport.
Efficient planning of journeys.

2. Coordination
Coordination between transport services in the area.
Coordination between transport services and individual day care units.
Identification of transport needs and resources in the area.
Review of passenger lists.
Transport brokerage - coordination of local resources and needs.
Vehicle sharing by day care service providers.

3. Administration
Zoning - transport for users from same area on same day.
Vehicles specific to day units.
Regular drivers/escorts for the same passengers.
Employment of drivers and escorts in day units during the day.
Use of vehicles for outings, journeys to clinics, shopping.
Flexible opening hours for day units; flexible journey times.
Reliable collection and return times.

4. Additional sources of transport and transport staff
Volunteer car services.
Taxi services.
Volunteer escorts for public transport.
Deregulated public flexible minibus services.
Community transport services.
Dial-a-ride or taxi card schemes.

5. Mobile and localised day care services
Travelling day hospitals/centres.
Mobile day care units.
Small local day centres in existing community buildings.
Rural day centres.
Local resource centres.
Day care by volunteers in private houses.

REFERENCES
1. J. Pahl, *Day services for elderly people in the Medway health district*, Health

140

services research unit, University of Kent, Canterbury, 1986
2. J.C. Brocklehurst and J.S. Tucker, *Progress in geriatric day care*, King's Fund, London, 1980, p 80
3. *Day hospitals in Gloucestershire: study carried out by management advisory service* (summary), Gloucester HA, 1986, p 6
4. G. Fennell, A.R. Emerson, M. Sidell and A. Hague, *Day centres for the elderly in East Anglia*, University of East Anglia School of Economic and Social Studies, Norwich, 1981, p 204
5. Pahl, *Day services for elderly people*, p 50
6. Brocklehurst and Tucker, *Progress in geriatric day care*, p 125
7. Pahl, *Day services for elderly people*, p 50
8. Fennell *et al*, *Day centres for the elderly*
9. Pahl, *Day services for elderly people*
10. D. Stokoe and G. Zuccollo, Travel sickness in patients attending a geriatric day hospital, *Age and Ageing*, 14, 5, 308–11
11. Stokoe and Zuccollo, Travel sickness, p 310
12. Fennell *et al*, *Day centres for the elderly*, p 204
13. A. Norman, *Transport and the elderly: problems and possible action*, National Corporation for the Care of Old People, London, 1977, p 77
14. Audit Commission, *Managing social services for the elderly more effectively*, HMSO, London, 1985
15. Norman, *Transport and the elderly*
16. S.M. Peace, *Caring from day to day*, MIND, London, 1980
17. Brocklehurst and Tucker, *Progress in geriatric day care*, p 181
18. Peace, *Caring from day to day*
19. Fennell *et al*, *Day centres for the elderly*
20. Pahl, *Day services for elderly people*
21. Pahl, *Day services for elderly people*
22. Pahl, *Day services for elderly people*
23. Greater London Association of Disabled People, *Transport in London for people with disabilities: Phase 1. Existing provision*, GLAD, London, 1984
24. R. Hedley and A. Norman, *Going places: two experiments in voluntary transport*, Centre for Policy on Ageing, London, 1984
25. Hedley and Norman, *Going places*
26. Hedley and Norman, *Going places*
27. GLAD, *Transport in London*
28. P. Hettiaratchy, The UK's travelling day hospital, *Ageing International*, 12, 2, 1985, 10–11
29. S. Kirkman, Moving with the times, *New Society*, 79, 1263, 1987, 27
30. P. Reed, A moving day centre filled with laughter, *Social Work Today*, 18, 21, 1987, 14–15
31. D. Challis and B. Davies, Long term care for the elderly: the Community Care Scheme, *British Journal of Social Work*, 15, 6, 1985, 563–79
32. R. Luckett and J. Braban, Creation and use of day care small groups, *Action Baseline*, Winter 1985, 17–18

8 Monitoring and evaluation of day care services

Introduction

How effective are the day care services currently offered? Such questions become increasingly important with the expansion of day care. A concomitant of the growing attention to day care issues has been an increased interest in how the services might be evaluated. As earlier studies have shown, the systematic evaluation of day care services is fairly complex. To evaluate a service using the 'rational' model entails specification of desired outcomes and of criteria for evaluation. This is not a simple matter when services and their objectives are not clearly defined and when the different groups involved have different and possibly conflicting priorities for the multiple aims of the service.

Evaluation methods, such as monitoring, measurement or experiment, may present difficulties when existing data collection or recording systems are unsophisticated and inconsistent. Where comparison between groups, settings or services is envisaged, controls are needed to ensure that like is compared with like. Cost-effectiveness studies are hampered by difficulties in obtaining accurate costings as well as in measuring outcomes. It is not surprising that earlier studies tended to rely on the apparently simpler method of consumer opinion surveys as a measure of the effectiveness of services.

In this chapter we describe not only the findings of earlier evaluative studies but also the methods used. Then we examine the ways in which day care services are monitored and evaluated at individual user, day care unit, local area, and national and regional levels. To help in planning approaches to evaluation we then summarise the methods which could be used at different levels.

Consumer opinion

The main research on day care services undertaken in the 1970s included interviews with consumers to measure satisfaction as part of wider studies which also used methods such as postal questionnaires, observation, and examination of records to describe the services in detail. The East Anglia study, for example, included long tape-recorded interviews with users.[1] Interviews were held with users, heads and staff in a sample of the NISW study[2] day units, and with patients, relatives and staff in 30 day hospitals for the research by Brocklehurst and Tucker.[3]

One non-interview study evaluated the use of a self-completion questionnaire by day hospital patients.[4] For each of 15 questions patients marked 'X' on a line to indicate their feelings on a scale, for example, from 'not enjoyable' to 'very enjoyable'. Comparison of results from questionnaires completed with and without the help of interviewers showed that the most reliable method was to use an interviewer. High scores for all questions suggested that patients found the day hospital satisfactory and were keen to attend again if necessary in the future. The self-completion questionnaire was quickly administered and easily analysed.

We have reviewed the main survey findings on consumer satisfaction in chapter 2 and elsewhere in this study, and indicated that they found a high level of satisfaction with the services. Analysis of elderly users' replies to a NISW study question about what attending the day unit had done for them classified the results as 'improvement', 'prevention', 'maintenance' and 'negative comments'; it was found that 'users of all types of centre were very unlikely to make negative comments and were most likely to make remarks suggesting that day centre attendance had "maintained" their function'.[5] Comparison between types of centre suggested that users of SSD centres to which most people came by transport were most likely to give favourable replies, and attenders of residentially based centres least likely to do so.

Surveys showed that the company and social contacts afforded by day care services were most highly valued by users of day centres and day hospitals; many users expressed appreciation of the staff. Benefits perceived by relatives or carers for themselves included both practical aspects such as the opportunity for activities and the emotional relief of a regular break. Levin and her colleagues found that supporters of confused elderly people valued day care services highly; their study suggested that day care reduced stress in supporters.[6] Relatives also considered that the elderly person benefited from attendance at the day care unit. Brocklehurst and Tucker reported that one-third of the relatives saw an improvement in the elderly person's physical condition.[7]

Although users' criticisms were few, the surveys nevertheless revealed specific complaints or dissatisfactions and made suggestions for improvements. As other writers have commented, it is difficult to interpret the meaning of expressed satisfaction, since consumers, particularly older ones, invariably respond to surveys in this way. Thus, although the consumer survey appears to be a simple method of evaluating services, there are difficulties in ensuring that findings are valid and accurately represent the views of older people. When asked about service preferences elderly people tend to reply in terms of what already exists. They are diffident consumers and may be afraid of making negative comments. Further, the sample of consumers should ideally be drawn from the whole population in order to include non-users of the services. As Carter points out, users are by definition satisfied to the extent that they still use the service, although this may result from family pressure to attend.[8]

For these reasons a form of dialogue other than the survey interview may be more appropriate as a way of eliciting users' real feelings. Participants at the CPA seminar suggested that feedback could be sought through good practice in daily relationships between staff and users; if those in face to face contact with users at the day unit could be encouraged to listen to what their users were really saying, they could be the people best placed to judge consumer response and convey this to service providers. One way of training staff for such practices and of eliciting staff views would be to hold small groups in which workers compared the present services with the kind of day care services they would want for themselves in future. This type of user feedback could be complemented by the occasional survey as part of an evaluation by an outside agency.

Measurement of effectiveness of services
Research which evaluated services using methods other than consumer opinion surveys consisted mainly of case studies of a particular unit or type of unit, rather than comparative studies.

Methods used ranged from the analysis of records to observation techniques, as shown by the following review.

The 16-week closure through industrial dispute of a geriatric day hospital provided the opportunity to study the effects of withdrawing this service.[9] Patients due to attend during the dispute were matched with control groups of patients for four years prior to and two years after the closure, and recorded data were analysed. It was found that the number of deaths and acute admissions increased significantly during the year of the dispute compared with the control years. But the study was based on small numbers and did not investigate which aspects of day hospital were beneficial.

The study of seven geriatric day hospitals in South Yorkshire (see chapter 2) used recorded data to determine how well day hospitals met their objectives.[10] The researchers measured inputs and processes such as sources of referral and typical patient days, and intermediate outcomes, for example throughput rates. They found that 'a better indication of performance is given by data on "intermediate outcomes" such as "social cases", throughput, occupancy, lengths of stay, rates of readmissions and destinations of patients when discharged'; where there were problems such as low staffing levels, the quality of care was affected and it was claimed that this was reflected for example in long stays and high readmission rates.

Patient assessment and follow-up was also used to measure effectiveness in day hospitals. In one prospective study 281 patients attending a geriatric day hospital over one year were initially assessed, then reviewed after one and three months.[11] Grading was based on a joint assessment by medical staff and therapists; further information was sought from relatives, home helps and community nurses. Day hospital care was found to be effective 'in improving mobility and self-care capacity, suggesting that patients with problems in these areas derive most benefit from attendance'.[12]

Another study compared the effectiveness of a new geriatric day hospital with existing services by randomly allocating 120 patients to day hospital and control groups.[13] The day hospital group attended two or three times a week for six to eight weeks whereas the control group received existing hospital and community care services. Patients were assessed at referral and after six weeks and five months. There was a significant improvement in day hospital patients' activities of daily living score at six weeks but this was not sustained at five months; however, there was a significant improvement in day hospital patients' mood after five months.

Another prospective study of 129 patients who were referred from the community to four psychogeriatric day hospitals in Lothian measured the effectiveness of services through home interviews with the patients' supporters, and follow-ups three to four and six to eight months later.[14] The results showed that supporters were more likely to continue their dependent's attendance at day hospital if they perceived that the dependent benefited greatly from it. The study also found that day hospital care reduced supporters' emotional distress, although there was no significant reduction in the patients' problems. This suggested that 'the significance of reduced levels of distress appears to be that it permits carers to continue giving care, while the converse—a failure to reduce the supporter's distress—seems to predict the breakdown of care and resulting institutionalisation'.[15]

A study of a day centre for elderly and physically handicapped people included interviews with 107 'drop-in' and 85 'referred' clients, a questionnaire about objectives to service managers, and the examination of attendance registers and SSD area records.[16] The findings showed that the centre met its objectives of providing a social centre with a friendly atmosphere; observations suggested that it also achieved its aim of blurring distinctions between groups of clients and between clients and helpers. Although the centre also aimed to prevent or postpone admission to residential care, the authors commented that the most dependent people, most likely to need residential care, were excluded from the centre.

A preliminary study to monitor the development of the Ringwood day care project (see chapter 6) used semi-structured tape-recorded interviews with those involved in the design and implementation of the project.[17] The respondents perceived a number of advantages of the scheme including respite for the elderly person and for carers, an increased choice in the type of care, postponing need for residential care, better coordination of community services, and greater involvement of the community in caring for elderly people. A need for training for home carers was identified, to help them provide greater stimulation for clients.

Smith and Cantley used 'pluralistic evaluation' to study the operation of a new psychogeriatric day hospital from different perspectives since they considered 'rationalistic' evaluation inappropriate to a developing service with a range of objectives.[18] They used several research methods, including interviews with professionals and administrators, attending meetings, study of hospital records, observation, interviews with relatives, and attending relatives' support groups. The study identified six criteria of success for the day hospital, which might conflict as different groups of staff interpreted success differently: 'the provision of an integrated service'; 'free patient flow'; 'clinical cure'; 'beneficial impact on related services'; 'support for relatives'; 'service of high quality'. The researchers found the most successful to be quality of service, which brought tangible benefits. The more ambitious aims, however, produced less obvious results. For example, it was found that coordination mechanisms may be counter-productive; that patient flow did not mean patient improvement; that few patients improved clinically; that relationships with other services varied; and that professionals did not always understand how relatives perceived their dependents' problems. Thus, on the whole, the researchers were ambivalent about the success of the day hospital.

A study of a psychogeriatric travelling day hospital also used pluralistic evaluation; the methods included using documents and routine statistics, semi-participant observation and interviews.[19] A number of different aims were identified and the researchers found successes such as a good quality service acceptable to patients, relatives and other professionals in an informal environment, with good transport arrangements, support for carers, and a working partnership between the agencies involved. There were problems in being a 'hospital outpost'; a physical base in the locality was recommended, together with greater autonomy from the parent hospital, so that the travelling day hospital could develop as a focal point for services for elderly mentally ill people in the community.

Outcomes of different types of care for elderly people were compared in a study using matched groups of users in day hospitals, in-patient wards, day centres and local authority homes in London.[20] The users were matched for age, sex, length of attendance, degree of dependence and probability of dementia, in each of the four types of care. One aspect of the study was a preliminary analysis of outcome by reassessment after nine months. No differences were found between types of care in mortality rates or dementia measures, but dependence ratings were found more likely to improve in day centres than in other settings including day hospitals.

Another part of this research was an observation study which aimed to find out what happened to users in each setting.[21] The technique used by observers included timing by bleepers every ten seconds to record activities and contacts; the method had a high level of reliability. In all four environments more than one-half of the time was spent sitting or lying down doing nothing. Time spent in occupational therapy or organised activities was much greater in day care units than residential settings, as was time spent in contact with others. People in day centres were found to spend more time (24%) on exercise, OT and treatment than those in day hospitals (18%), and to have a much lower proportion than all other settings of individuals who spent more than one-half of their time in isolated inactivity. This comparative study is helpful in showing how day hospitals and day centres performed in relation to each other and to other settings. There are, unfortunately, few such studies.

Studies of costs and cost-effectiveness
We have mentioned in chapters 2 and 5 the difficulties of accurately costing day care services. As Martin and Millard pointed out, day hospital care is not cheap; salaries, buildings and maintenance, ambulances and the cost of domiciliary health and social services have to be taken into account.[22] The East Anglia study found that in 47 of 320 cases institutional care may have been avoided by the use of day care, but that this did not necessarily imply a cost saving because day care and domiciliary services were also expensive.[23]

Research based on the NISW study data compared cost-effectiveness of different day care sectors: cost and income data were collected for units for elderly people in the NISW sample areas, and a 'cost function technique' was used to standardise costs.[24] Capital costs were not measured. Economies of scale were found in the statutory health and social services sectors where the average cost per attendance was lower in larger units. In the voluntary sector small-scale units could provide the service more cheaply than other sectors, but this did not apply to larger voluntary units which may have found difficulty in attracting volunteers.

Other studies of costs and cost-effectiveness were all of geriatric day hospitals. Ross estimated the cost per patient per day in 1973–74 as £6 (including £2 ambulance costs) and compared this with residential care (£28 per week), teaching hospital (£140 per week) and geriatric hospital (£49 per week); day hospital care was thus more expensive than residential care for a patient attending five days per week, and more expensive than geriatric in-patient care if costs of other services for a person living alone were included.[25] Another study compared day hospital costs of £34 per week (for 2.5 attendances per patient) plus £13 community support, with in-patient costs of £130 per week.[26] Since assessment of patients by day hospital staff on discharge found that one-third had improved and one-quarter had been maintained, the study concluded that the day hospital was effective and saved money compared with in-patient treatment. Irvine calculated that capital costs for a day hospital place and an in-patient bed were similar, but commented that the day hospital place would help seven times as many patients; costs per day were also similar but patients attended the day hospital for only three days a week.[27]

The study by Tucker and colleagues described earlier found that, over five months, rehabilitation cost more for the day hospital patients than for the control group; and that day hospital care, costing slightly less per day than in-patient care, was for a longer period and thus more expensive than in-patient care and domiciliary rehabilitation.[28] The authors concluded that day hospital care should not be seen as a 'cheap alternative' and that there should be adequate in-patient facilities, domiciliary services and day care centres.

A review of studies on day hospital costs found that day hospitals were expensive, but used skilled staff effectively.[29] The advantages identified were that each day hospital place could help to keep 2½ patients in the community; that day hospital care was preferred by patients; that informal carers were involved and that they were 'cost-effective' because their contribution was 'free'. Others, however, argued that the costs to the carer must be taken into account. Donaldson and colleagues criticised the existing cost-effective studies and proposed a four stage study of the cost-effectiveness of day hospital care: random allocation of patients to day hospitals and other forms of care; costing of all services over a set period; collection of outcome data and consumer satisfaction measures; and comparison of costs and outcomes for each group.[30]

None of the consumer opinion, evaluation or cost-effectiveness studies described above provides an entirely satisfactory evaluation of day care services. All the studies, however, found day hospitals or centres beneficial to some extent, and some identified areas where they were less successful. There is a need for more well-designed comparative and cost-effectiveness studies using a variety of methods so that day care services may be evaluated in the context of other community care and residential services. Small-scale local comparative studies would prove useful for service providers and planners, while national studies would facilitate government policy making and guidance.

Monitoring of individual users
The first level of monitoring of day care services is that of the individual user. If day care services are to become more flexible and geared to individual needs, then an integral part of such services should be careful initial assessment followed by periodic reviews of the programme's effectiveness in meeting assessed needs. For the very dependent user there would ideally be joint multi-disciplinary assessment and review for the whole range of community care services.

As we have shown in chapter 4, however, assessment much depended on the service for which the elderly person applied or was referred; and admission criteria and assessment procedures varied between service types and providers. Detailed assessment before or on admission to the unit was much more likely for day hospitals, specialist day units and some SSD day care services than for other voluntary and statutory day centres. The present separate systems of assessment mean that there is considerable overlap between the sectors of day care services in the level of dependence of the users.

The examples of strategic documents sent to CPA (see chapter 6) showed that some authorities were moving in the direction of joint assessment for community care packages, with plans for joint assessment and services to be coordinated by a care manager or key worker for each individual. The importance of regular review or reassessment was emphasised in strategy documents, although we received few examples of how such reviews were carried out.

As earlier studies have shown, monitoring of individual users' progress was a feature of day hospital care but less widespread in day centres. Day hospitals had regular multi-disciplinary review meetings, usually held weekly and involving community professionals as well as the day hospital team, and sometimes the patient and relatives. At such meetings participants discussed the progress of selected individuals whose cases were due for review. The frequency of reviews varied according to the type of treatment and care; they were likely to be held more often where short-term rehabilitation was the aim. The review meeting decided, for instance, whether the patient was ready to be discharged, or whether any charges should be made to the components of the individual care programme.

Several SSDs included review procedures in the policy documents sent to CPA. Typically, a review panel would be convened, chaired by the supervisor or officer-in-charge of the day care unit, and including any professionals involved, for example social worker or community nurse; the client and relatives would usually be invited to attend. Such reviews were normally held within one or two months of admission, then at three- or six-monthly intervals. The review monitored the effectiveness of care programmes, and decided whether attendance should continue, and whether the number of weekly attendances or particular items in the programme should be changed. Setting goals to be met by the time of the next review was another feature of some procedures.

One aspect of assessment and review which did not receive much attention in the policy documents was that of record keeping. Where this was mentioned, it was stated that the proceedings and recommendations would be recorded and added to the individual user's records. We have very little information about how the reviews were actually conducted, what was recorded, in what way and when, how reliable the records were and who had access to them. Such questions will be increasingly important if joint assessment and review become more widespread, particularly when computerised records are used. Reliable, consistent recording systems with safeguards for individual confidentiality are also essential to the effective monitoring of services at day care unit level.

Monitoring and evaluation at day care unit level
At individual unit level day care services may be monitored in a number of ways. First, there should be routine monitoring of attendances, including follow-up of non-attenders, and records on new users and referral sources, discharges and reasons for leaving. Services vary in the extent to which such basic records are kept; the more socially oriented centres, particularly in the voluntary sector, are less likely to have recording systems for such information. Second, transport services should be monitored regularly to identify difficulties. Basic information on numbers of transport users, types of transport used, journey times and arrival and departure times, would be helpful, together with regular reviews of passenger lists. Third, a record could be made of the actual group activities carried out, to complement the records of individual users' programmes.

Apart from such routine monitoring, there could be occasional evaluations of the running of the unit as a whole, preferably by outside evaluators. Such evaluations would look at the objectives of the unit and how these were met, study the roles played by administrators, professional and care workers and volunteers, and the participation of users and carers; examine the effectiveness of transport services; calculate costs; and collect the opinions of users, carers and staff. Once the evaluation is completed and recommendations made, the findings should be communicated to all those concerned so that lessons from the study may be widely learned and commitment generated to implement recommendations.

In general, replies to CPA's letter did not contain much information on how services were monitored at day care unit level;

this was not specifically requested. There were, however, some examples of studies undertaken at different types of unit.

The Kershaw day centre in Fareham, run by Fareham district voluntary support group with two paid staff, a supervisor and driver/handyman, and 50 to 60 volunteers, was opened in 1980. As part of a review of day centres by Hampshire SSD, and as requested by the management committee, a research study was carried out to clarify what the day centre meant to participants and evaluate its effectiveness.[31] The methods used were examination of records, participant observation, interviews with users, volunteers, supervisor and chairman, and group discussion with professionals who referred users to the centre. The study found that the centre was much appreciated by users, but areas for improvement were identified. In spite of unmet demand the centre was underoccupied because of transport difficulties. The contribution of volunteers could be developed and their roles more clearly defined; recommendations included meetings to exchange views and training for new volunteers. Too much was expected of the supervisor whose tasks, it was suggested, should be shared.

A study on the Williams day hospital, Harlow, used examination of statistics and discussions with individuals and groups.[32] The data routinely collected for the DHSS showed low occupancy of the 40-place unit and a low proportion of new patients. Discussions revealed that although day hospital activities should be geared to rehabilitation, the level of activities was low and the unit tended to be used as a day centre. Transport problems prevented development and there was little liaison with other community services. The report emphasised that the staff worked hard but that the unit was understaffed and problems arose from the philosophy and organisation of the unit. It was recommended that there should be regular reviews and a discharge policy, and emphasis on active rehabilitation; and that further evaluation should be based on routine collection of detailed information for each patient. Many of the recommendations of this study have since been implemented.

A review of St Richard's day hospital, Chichester HA, was undertaken to evaluate the day hospital and provide feedback to staff.[33] Interviews were held with staff and patients, a census of one week's activities was taken, information was requested from GPs and community nurses, and statistics were collected. This study also found underuse of the day hospital in spite of demand for places, and identified problems with a rigid referral procedure and lack of discharge policy. There were difficulties in organising patients' time, unpredictable transport times, lack of communication between different groups of staff, and high staff turnover. The report recommended allowing direct referrals by GPs and community nurses for a trial period and encouraging more referrals, more intensive therapy, and better information for patients and relatives.

The Oundle community care unit, which operated a day and night centre, was set up by Kettering HA with funding from the DHSS initiative to develop services for mental illness in old age, and was evaluated by Northamptonshire County Council.[34] The combination of methods used comprised assessment schedules and data on attendances; reassessment of carers' stress after receiving the service; tape-recorded interviews with a small sample of carers; periodic review of 20 cases; a survey of over 75s in the community; and a Program Analysis of Service Systems (PASS) evaluation by a team of evaluators using observation, interviews, discussions and examination of documents. The study found that the service was successful in reaching those in need but that the local prevalence of dementia was lower than expected and thus clients with more social needs and physical disabilities had been accepted. Carers' stress had been reduced and carers valued the service and the staff. There was little emphasis on clinical cure of patients or individual care plans and activities were limited. Thus the unit operated more as a social day centre than a specialist unit; the report suggested that it could be run by social services or a voluntary agency at lower cost.

The Babington day unit, Southern Derbyshire, was jointly planned, financed, operated and managed by the SSD and HA and provided 25 places for medical and social assessment, rehabilitation and/or care of elderly people. An evaluation examined policy documents and records, compared costs with other projects, interviewed staff and users, and sent postal questionnaires to professionals who referred users.[35] The study found a lack of clarity in the objectives and operational details; it showed that staff were unsure about the management structure and their roles; that one-third of potential referrers were unclear about the functions of the unit; and that costs were excessive because of the low occupancy rate. Users and carers, however, found the service useful although there had been little reduction in users' dependence. A further three-month review was recommended to reassess the objectives, structure and function of the unit.

Consumer opinion surveys carried out in the course of a number of local studies generally found that users were very positive about the day care unit and valued the social contacts, social events and outings, the staff and the provision of meals and personal care services. Many users were reluctant to criticise the services; this applied especially to the more handicapped users, as pointed out in a conference report from the London Borough of Sutton. The criticisms voiced by users concerned transport, lack of activities or boring activities. Suggestions usually focused on the desire of a substantial minority to attend more often, including at weekends, and on additional activities which might be introduced, such as crafts, music and drama, and advice services. Carers were also very appreciative of day care services and valued the break for themselves and an improvement in their dependent's morale, but would have preferred longer opening hours and more frequent attendances. They usually suggested improved transport services and more information and advice.

The staff and community professionals interviewed identified benefits to users such as social contacts, giving meaning or structure to their lives, the personal services provided, and opportunities for outings, as well as relief for carers. Criticisms focused on inadequate stimulation, low therapeutic content, transport, limited hours, and lack of provision for the most dependent users. Suggested improvements were a wider range of activities, more frequent attendances, extending opening hours and providing weekend services, more therapeutic and medical services, and improved transport.

The day care services were thus valued although difficulties were identified from consumer opinion surveys and evaluation studies. The studies described above are intended to illustrate the evaluation of different types of unit, but cannot be considered representative. We have little information on the prevalence of such evaluative studies but the response to the CPA trawl suggests that they are infrequent and perhaps more likely to be carried out when there are problems with particular units or when special funding has been granted to an innovative project.

Evaluation studies may be considered expensive by service providers with competing priorities for resources but should be seen in the context of the operating costs of the services, particularly for the more expensive day hospitals and specialist units. The routine monitoring of records, however, should not be too demanding of resources once the systems are in operation. Such records could then be used as a basis for regular reviews of the operation of the service by groups of staff, as held by some of the statutory units on which we received information.

Monitoring and evaluation at local area level
Again, at local level, monitoring may be of routinely collected records or by specially conducted studies or reviews. The services may be monitored by health or social services authorities or voluntary agencies separately, or a joint study may be undertaken. As we have seen in chapter 6 authorities are beginning to conduct joint reviews of all the day care services in their areas. Even if studies are undertaken by one agency, the services of other local agencies should be taken into account as the services impinge on each other.

The responsibility for monitoring day care services is clear in the case of those directly provided or financially supported by one agency. For the non-statutory sectors, however, and for jointly funded or provided services, or localised services using community premises such as sheltered housing units, it is necessary for one agency to take the lead in reviewing the overall provision. There is a consensus that this is a role for the social services department or for a joint body of statutory and voluntary representatives.

Where the voluntary sector is concerned, the SSD has a particular role in monitoring the effectiveness of day care services which it supports financially. As shown in chapter 5 such monitoring has often been tokenistic, consisting of receiving annual reports and accounts, representation on management committees, and occasional visits by officers or members. In the interests of accountability and of service development there is a more active role for SSD officers in monitoring what actually happens in grant-aided centres. Further, this could usefully be extended to the whole of voluntary and SSD provision with guidance being offered on development of services and on how units might monitor their own services.

Where routine monitoring at local area level is concerned, there are certain statistics collected for returns to the DHSS, and local profiles and packages of indicators are available (see below). Such quantitative indicators are used by authorities to monitor their own services and compare them with those of other areas. Where indicators are available at unit level, authorities may compare the services of individual day units. Since the introduction of the new Körner information system designed to record information that DHAs need to make management decisions, DHAs will have more information than before on day hospitals. The Körner minimum data set on day hospitals should contain not only quantitative data for returns to the DHSS, but also information about individual day care units and their availability and operational policies.

The extent to which authorities collect and monitor other data on day care services varies; we have received little information on this topic. It seems essential, however, for all authorities to have adequate basic information about all aspects of the services in order to formulate policies and plan for future directions of day care services, rather than allowing continued ad hoc development and increasing expenditure on services which may not be the most effective way of meeting changing needs.

Such basic information would include updated lists of all day care services in the area with details of facilities, activities and services offered. Monitoring transport provision and transport use and costs for all local day care services would also be a priority. From time to time authorities could reassess day care needs for the area and evaluate how well current provision met those needs. The actual activities carried out in units, as compared with stated policy, could be monitored. Consumer opinion on day care services, including that of users and non-users, carers and staff, could be collected. In particular, as suggested above, comparative studies of the effectiveness of different units in the same or other sectors, and comparisons of costs and cost-effectiveness would be useful. Again, it is important that those involved in individual units receive feedback about the findings of such studies and that recommendations are implemented. The use of day conferences or seminars for staff, volunteers and users is also effective in disseminating research findings and collecting consumer opinion.

In response to CPA's letter we received some examples of ways in which statutory authorities were monitoring or evaluating day care services in their areas, for instance the local reviews of day care services mentioned in chapter 6. We illustrate below methods of monitoring and evaluation which formed part of the monitoring process of different authorities.

The London Borough of Kensington and Chelsea SSD monitored statistics on day centres and other services and prepared an annual performance monitoring report and quarterly trend analysis reports. The annual performance report gave, for each day centre and for all day centres, the average daily attendance together with figures for capacity and target numbers of places, unit costs at 100% occupancy, numbers on the register and target numbers. The trend analysis report included numbers on the register, average daily attendance and occupancy for each quarter, and showed the average, high and low figures for the past five years, two years and recent year, and seasonal averages.

In Norfolk, SSD research officers visited six day centres and reported on the main issues identified, as part of a review of services for elderly people. Subsequently, more work on day care philosophy, policies and practices has been carried out and a departmental philosophy and guidance for day centres have been drafted. As part of a review of community day care in West Wiltshire, a survey was carried out and a list produced of all day care centres with details of time and place, area served, organiser and treasurer, and further information on sources of meals, attendances, expansion possibilities, analysis of referrals, transport and welfare facilities, volunteers, and charges.

In Stockport a review of community-based day centres and luncheon clubs was coordinated by a group of representatives from the SSD and voluntary agencies, with subgroups to examine five topics: transport, meals, support, volunteers, and members. A questionnaire was sent to all centres and clubs on these topics, and included dependence rating of members. In

Croydon, where all day care services were run by the voluntary sector, a survey was undertaken for the SSD of ten voluntary day centres and pop-ins which were open at least five days a week. The centres were visited and interviews held with organisers and other informants, usually committee members, covering a wide range of topics.

The London Borough of Sutton has recently reviewed day care services and evaluated them by conducting a small research project to collect consumer, professional and public opinion about day care services, recommend changes and improvements and identify unmet needs. The results were presented at a day conference for staff from voluntary and statutory agencies, carers and users.

A management advisory service report was produced on day hospitals in Gloucestershire for Gloucester HA and Cheltenham and district HA. This was the first phase of a study to examine whether day hospitals and transport were being used effectively. The second phase will be a more intensive study of problems identified by the report, to be carried out, in Gloucester HA, under the auspices of a review group for services to elderly people. Other HAs planned to undertake research on the effectiveness of day hospitals.

The findings of such studies on various topics have already been mentioned in previous chapters and will by now be familiar. For example, studies found uneven geographical distribution, unclear objectives, transport difficulties, the need to develop the range of activities and offer more flexible services, and to coordinate the services of different agencies.

Monitoring and evaluation at national and regional levels
Local and health authorities make annual returns to the DHSS of data on day care units and places. Since the introduction of the Körner information system the NHS returns now include more data on day hospitals than previously collected. A new form introduced in 1987–88 on the availability and use of facilities in NHS day care collects from each DHA the following data on geriatric and psychogeriatric day units aggregated at district level: the number of place days available, the number of regular day attenders on the register, numbers of first attendances and reattendances of day attenders during the year,

and numbers of first attendances and reattendances of in-patients at the day hospital. Data for 1987–88 were not available in time for this study, but will be published in due course by the DHSS. Such statistical data are used by the DHSS for monitoring individual districts through the regional health authorities (RHAs) as part of the annual review process.

Local authority annual returns to the DHSS on day centres comprise an annually updated gazeteer with information for each centre on the name and address, centre status, client group and number of places, together with the LA and HA districts; and a separate form which collects the number of day centre places within LA residential homes for elderly and physically handicapped people, and limited information on places made available to LAs by other sectors. Statistics based on these returns are published annually. Local authority profiles are also produced by DHSS statisticians for DHSS and LA use in monitoring services. Data are also collected and published by CIPFA. The present system of DHSS returns is unsatisfactory as it provides little information on use of the LA centres, and does not include voluntary and private sector day centres, which makes it difficult to estimate the level and spread of provision, as shown in chapter 4. A revised statistical return which would collect more detail on day centres is under consideration by the DHSS.

The data from central returns and other national sources are used to produce national packages of indicators of authorities' service provision which can be displayed in graphical form on screen. Performance indicators (PIs) for the NHS, used in the annual review process, have recently been revised; a report on the new PIs was due to be published in late 1988. The main PIs currently used which relate to day hospital care are the geriatric day patient attendance rate (the annual number of total attendances related to the DHA's population aged 75 and over), and the percentage of new geriatric day patients (the annual number of first-time attendances as a percentage of all attendances by geriatric day patients).

The guidance for users of the PI package gives advice on the use and interpretation of PIs in the context of local circumstances. It also includes a checklist on community care of elderly people, suggested to complement the quantitative indicators which do not measure quality or outcome. A consultation paper on PIs for services for elderly people advocated the use of such checklists locally to assess quality of care; work was also being undertaken elsewhere on a checklist for 'achievable standards' of care for elderly people.[36] The consultation paper recognised the need for site level indicators which would, for instance, allow individual day hospitals to assess their services.

The DHSS social services inspectorate has developed, in collaboration with the LA associations, a set of key indicators (KIs) of LA social services, to be issued to each SSD late in 1988. This will be a demonstration package using data for 1984–85 to illustrate the concepts and graphical form of the indicators before updated KIs are produced. Indicators on day care services for elderly people in a local authority will be expenditure on day care as a percentage of all spending on services to elderly and disabled people; gross expenditure on day care for elderly people per person aged 65 and over; number of day care places in centres for elderly people and mixed centres per 1,000 aged 65 and over; and gross expenditure on day care for elderly and disabled people per week per place provided in centres for elderly people and mixed centres.

The limitations of such quantified indicators were recognised both by those who devised them and by other commentators. As the national packages use data aggregated at LA or HA level they do not reflect differences between units. Caution must be used in their interpretation, and they should be set in the context of other local services and central government policies. Allen and his colleagues pointed out that PIs measure activity and resources rather than performance or quality of services; that they are based on national data which are inaccurate; and that they may be used to compare areas which are not comparable.[37] They concluded, however, that PIs serve a useful purpose in the absence of better measures.

The development of indicators has been an integral part of recent government activity to improve monitoring of the efficiency of services. Indicators provide a starting point for examining very basic information about authorities' services within a national framework, and make use of the limited data from central returns. The collection of more detailed national statistics and the further refinement of indicators should increase the usefulness of this type of monitoring. It is, however, necessary at national, as at other levels, to use more qualitative evaluation of the effectiveness of services. As suggested above there is a need for national comparative studies and cost-effectiveness studies of different types of day care service. The evaluation carried out to date has been limited and piecemeal.

Bodies such as the RHAs, the SSI, the Audit Commission, the Health Advisory Service, and research and policy divisions of the DHSS, all have a role in carrying out or commissioning reviews or research studies of various aspects of day care services, and disseminating their findings. The present research, for example, was commissioned by the DHSS, as were the area studies carried out in East Anglia and Birmingham.[38,39] In the South West region the SSI organised and reported on two seminars, held in December 1987 and October 1988, to promote discussion of day care issues by managers and service providers from statutory and voluntary agencies.[40] Trent RHA held a similar seminar in November 1988.

The monitoring and evaluation carried out at national and regional levels tends, however, to be geared to one service or another with different agencies or branches of the same agency looking at day centre or day hospital services. There is no national forum for information, research, discussion and policy development on day care services as a whole, a gap which has become increasingly noticeable during the course of this study. Such is our anxiety about this situation that, in chapter 9, we shall address the matter more fully.

Methods of monitoring and evaluation
We summarise below the main methods by which day care services may be monitored and evaluated at different levels.

1. Individual user level
Initial assessment for day care service.
Regular reviews of progress in day care programme.
Multi-disciplinary assessment for community care services.
Care manager or key worker system.
Regular reviews of success of day care as part of community care.
Multi-disciplinary review meetings.
Detailed records on individual user.

2. Day care unit level

Routine monitoring
Reliable consistent recording system.
Monitoring of attendances, follow-up of non-attenders.
Monitoring of new users and referral sources.
Monitoring and follow-up of leavers.
Monitoring of transport services.
Monitoring of group activities.
Regular staff reviews of unit operation.

Consumer opinion
Self-completion questionnaires for users, carers, staff, other
    professionals.
Interviews with users, carers, staff, other professionals.
Face to face contact between workers, volunteers and users.
Group discussions for day care staff and other community
    professionals.

Internal or external evaluation studies by combination of methods
Analysis of records and operational policies.
Interview or assessment and follow-up of users and carers.
Interviews or questionnaires for staff, other community
    professionals.
Attendance at meetings, carers' groups.
Observation techniques.
Study of costs and cost-effectiveness.
Feedback of findings of evaluation.

3. Local area level

Routine monitoring and review
Recording and monitoring of data on unit places, occupancy
    and costs.
Updated detailed lists of day care services in area.
Monitoring of transport services and costs.
Monitoring of activities in units.
Guidance to units on how to monitor own services.
Review of day care services and needs by SSD, DHA or
    voluntary agency.
Joint review of services by two or more agencies.

Consumer opinion
Self-completion questionnaires for users, carers, staff, other professionals.
Interviews with users, carers, staff, other professionals.
Group meetings and seminars.

Internal or external evaluation studies by combination of methods
Examination of statistical data.
Interview or assessment and follow-up of users and carers.
Interviews or questionnaires for staff and other professionals.
Attendance at meetings, carers' groups.
Observation techniques.
Comparative studies of units' or sectors' effectiveness.
Comparative studies of costs and cost-effectiveness.
Feedback findings of evaluation eg. day conferences and seminars.

4. National and regional levels
Collection of reliable detailed statistics for all sectors.
Monitoring of authorities' provision.
Development of indicator packages.
In-house or commissioned research.
Comparative studies of effectiveness and cost-effectiveness.
Dissemination of research findings.
National/regional seminars and conferences.

REFERENCES
1. G. Fennell, A.R. Emerson, M. Sidell and A. Hague, *Day centres for the elderly in East Anglia*, University of East Anglia School of Economic and Social Studies, Norwich, 1981
2. J. Carter, *Day services for adults—somewhere to go*, George Allen and Unwin, London, 1981
3. J.C. Brocklehurst and J.S. Tucker, *Progress in geriatric day care*, King's Fund, London, 1980
4. H. Peach and M. Pathy, Evaluation of patients' assessment of day hospital care, *British Journal of Preventive and Social Medicine*, 31, 1977, 209–10
5. C. Edwards, I. Sinclair and P. Gorbach, Day centres for the elderly: variations in type, provision and user response, *British Journal of Social Work*, 10, 4, 1980, 426
6. E. Levin, I. Sinclair and P. Gorbach, *The supporters of confused elderly people at home*, National Institute for Social Work, London, 1983
7. Brocklehurst and Tucker, *Progress in geriatric day care*
8. Carter, *Day services for adults*
9. P. Berrey, Increase in acute admissions and deaths after closing a geriatric day hospital, *British Medical Journal*, 292, 1986, 176–78

164

10. C. Donaldson, K. Wright and A. Maynard, *Utilisation and performance of day hospitals for the elderly in South Yorkshire*, a report to the Trent Regional Health Authority by the Centre for Health Economics, University of York, 1985, ch 7

11. W.J. Maclennan,, U.K. Ghosh and R.T. Ritchie, How does a day hospital work?, *Health Bulletin*, 43, 3, 1985, 109–16

12. Maclennan *et al*, How does a day hospital work?, p 115

13. M.A. Tucker, J.G. Davidson and S.J. Ogle, Day hospital rehabilitation—effectiveness and cost in the elderly: a randomised controlled trial, *British Medical Journal*, 289, 1984, 1209–12

14. C.J. Gilleard, E. Gilleard and J.E. Whittick, Impact of psychogeriatric day hospital care on the patient's family, *British Journal of Psychiatry*, 145, 1984, 487–92

15. C.J. Gilleard, Influence of emotional distress among supporters on the outcome of psychogeriatric day care, *British Journal of Psychiatry*, 150, 1987, 222

16. P. Fletcher and J. Robinson, *Desborough Hall: study of a day centre*, Buckinghamshire County Council Social Services Department, 1974

17. C. Adcock, *The Ringwood day care project*, Hampshire County Council SSD research section, 1985

18. G. Smith and C. Cantley, *Pluralistic evaluation: a study in day care for the elderly mentally infirm*, a brief summary report of some problems associated with the evaluation of a new psychogeriatric day hospital, University of Glasgow, Glasgow, 1983

19. N. Evans, I. Kendall, R. Lovelock and J. Powell, *Something to look forward to: an evaluation of a travelling day hospital for elderly mentally ill people*, Social Services Research and Intelligence Unit, Portsmouth, 1986

20. A.J.D. Macdonald, A.H. Mann, R. Jenkins, L. Richard, C. Godlove and G. Rodwell, Preliminary communication. An attempt to determine the impact of four types of care upon the elderly in London by the study of matched groups, *Psychological medicine*, 12, 1982, 193–200

21. C. Godlove, L. Richard and G. Rodwell, *Time for action: an observation study of elderly people in four different care environments*, University of Sheffield Joint Unit for Social Services Research and Community Care, Sheffield, 1982

22. A. Martin and P.H. Millard, *Day hospitals for the elderly; therapeutic or social?*, St George's Hospital, London, 1978

23. Fennell *et al*, *Day centres for the elderly*

24. M. Knapp and S. Missiakoulis, Inter-sectoral cost comparisons: day care for the elderly, *Journal of Social Policy*, 11, 3, 1982, 335–54

25. D.N. Ross, Geriatric day hospitals: counting the cost compared with other methods of support, *Age and Ageing*, 5, 1976, 171–75

26. J.P.R. MacFarlane, T. Collings, K. Graham and J.C. MacIntosh, Day hospitals in modern clinical practice—cost benefit, *Age and Ageing*, 8, 1979, supplement, 80–86

27. R.E. Irvine, Geriatric day hospitals: present trends, *Health Trends*, 12, 1980, 68–71

28. Tucker *et al*, Day hospital rehabilitation

29. M. Hildick-Smith, Geriatric day hospitals—changing emphasis in costs, *Age and Ageing*, 13, 1984, 95–100

30. C. Donaldson, K. Wright and A. Maynard, Determining value for money in day hospital care for the elderly, *Age and Ageing*, 15, 1986, 1–7

31. R. Webber, *Report on Kershaw day centre Fareham*, Social Services Research and Intelligence Unit, Portsmouth, 1983

32. J. Watson, *A report on the Williams day hospital Harlow*, Department of Community Medicine, West Essex HA, 1986

33. Chichester HA, *A review of St Richard's day hospital for the elderly*, Chichester, 1987

34. R. Gibbins, *Oundle community care unit: an evaluation of an initiative in the care of the elderly mentally infirm*, Central Policy and Research Unit, Northamptonshire County Council, Northampton, 1986

35. M. Bretman, *An evaluation of the work of the Babington day unit*, Department of Community Medicine, Southern Derbyshire HA, in association with Social Services Research and Information Section, Derby, 1986

36. Performance indicators for the NHS, Performance indicator group, *Services for the elderly*, consultation paper no. 8, DHSS, London 1987

37. D. Allen, M. Harley and G.T. Makinson, Performance indicators in the National Health Service, *Social Policy and Administration*, 21, 1987, 70–84

38. Fennell *et al*, *Day centres for the elderly*

39. R. Bowl, H. Taylor, M. Taylor and N. Thomas, *Day care for the elderly in Birmingham*, University of Birmingham Social Services Unit, Birmingham 1978

40. C. Shipley, *South West workshop on day centres for elderly people*, Social Services Inspectorate, DHSS, Norfolk House, Bristol, 1988

9 Conclusions and recommendations

Introduction: the benefits of day care services

Day care services are warmly appreciated by their users, informal carers, day care workers, and the professionals who refer older people to them, as shown by this and earlier studies. Users enjoy attending day care units for the social contacts and services, and their physical and mental condition is sometimes improved thereby, for example through increased morale, or mobility and self-care skills. Carers of the more dependent users enjoy relief from the constant responsibility of caring. This allows them to rest, go shopping, pursue leisure activities, catch up with chores, or, occasionally, to work part-time or full-time outside the home. Research has shown that carers' stress has been reduced by their dependents' attendance at day units, and that they have been able to continue caring as a result. Paid and volunteer staff gain satisfaction from working in day care services, and other community professionals find these services of value in helping dependent older people to live in the community.

If day care services were withdrawn, there would be considerable disadvantages, such as increased admissions to hospital and residential care, and increased pressure on domiciliary and fieldwork services and on carers. Day care services should not be seen as an alternative to these other services but as complementary to them and forming an essential component of community care.

This study has shown that current day care provision is a very complex matter with many issues to be considered. It is not surprising that there are difficulties in day care service provision. In this chapter we summarize the study's main findings on the most salient issues, offer conclusions on the key questions identified, and make recommendations as to the development of day care services to meet the needs of older people in the 1990s. The first question is that of definitions and objectives.

How could day care services be defined and what objectives could they serve?

Day care services as currently defined span a very broad area and meet a wide range of needs. This study has identified a need for greater clarity in the definition of day care services. They are frequently advocated as beneficial for individuals or particular 'need' groups among elderly people, without adequate attention to the specific aspects of the service from which these people could benefit. The present loose definition has meant that there are overlaps between the services offered by different agencies and, more seriously, that there are groups of very dependent elderly people, those most in need of day care services, to whom these services are least accessible. It seems appropriate to consider some redistribution of the services and question some assumptions about their objectives.

The aims of day care services have been shown to be diverse and sometimes conflicting, a consequence of the varied interests involved. The objectives of the authorities that responded to CPA's trawl were, on the whole, neither well distinguished nor clearly stated (see chapter 3). We suggest that definitions and objectives should be formulated using the categories listed at the end of chapter 3. A major objective of both SSDs and HAs was prevention: that day care services should help older people to remain in their own homes in the community. For day centres SSDs tended to cite the aim of providing social care and company, which had low priority among HAs' aims for day hospitals. The most frequently stated aim for day hospitals was rehabilitation and treatment, in turn not a high priority for day centres. The differences between day centres and day hospitals in other aims were less marked. Research has shown that, despite the stated objectives, a comparatively low proportion of users' time, even in day hospitals, is spent in therapeutic activities.

Where social objectives of day care services are concerned, these services are often seen as a panacea for the relief of isolation and loneliness. Partly for this reason purely social and leisure facilities such as lunch clubs and social day centres are often included in the definition of day care services. We should, however, question the assumption that day care services will automatically reduce loneliness. This belief may be based on a lack of appreciation of the differences between social isolation, the objective state of having few social contacts, and the subjective experience of loneliness. As Carter pointed out, day care services provide 'company and sociability' rather than 'intimacy'.[1] To reduce loneliness, close intimate relationships are needed. Day care units are not necessarily the best places to form such relationships. Fennell and his colleagues emphasised that 'centres can alleviate loneliness and can help to offset the effects of bereavement but only in carefully specified circumstances which can be summarised as a conscious attempt to make the centre meaningful to the user'.[2]

There are other social, leisure and educational facilities which older people could attend, where they could be involved in meaningful activities with other people of their own or other age groups, and form close relationships. We find the association between older age, loneliness, and day care services unhelpful. It seems to advocate that older people should be taken out of normal community life and receive their social contacts in separate places. Carter suggested that such assumptions may reflect society's attitudes to ageing and posed the question, 'To what extent do understandings in day units collude with the dislocation of the old from their social fabric?[3]

For such reasons we excluded purely social and educational facilities from our operational definition of day care services and included only those where people attend for most of the day and are offered care in the sense of some form of therapeutic, social or medical attention or support. The operational definition formulated to meet one of the first aims of the study was as follows: *A day care service offers communal care, with paid or voluntary care givers present, in a setting outside the user's own home. Individuals come or are brought to use the services, which are available for at least four hours during the day, and return home on the same day.*

The findings of this study suggest the need for a tighter definition of day care services for three main reasons. First, it would lead to greater clarity in policy making and in administrative processes such as assessment and referral for day care services. Second, it would help to ensure that the specialised services are available for those who need them most. Third, it would further the interests of giving older people more choice and access to normal facilities.

We therefore recommend that *day care services* be distinguished from *day facilities*. Day care services as designed above would fulfil a more specialised function than day care as currently defined, and take a more systematic approach to the individual. The therapeutic and supportive objectives would be much more central than they are now. We suggest that the main objectives of these services should be:

1. short-term social and medical assessment, treatment, rehabilitation and therapy
2. longer-term maintenance and monitoring, and relief for carers.

They should not be used as a substitute for residential care when this is really needed by the elderly person and/or carer.

Day care services would be offered to people with assessed needs for them, who would then also receive all the benefits of socialising, company and stimulating activities which are a valued part of day care. For those whose main needs are for company, however, we would define the services as *day facilities*, which would include social day facilities such as day clubs and lunch clubs offered at present by social services and voluntary organisations. Goldberg and Connolly suggested a similar distinction between the day care centre and the senior citizen centre.[4] But we should also like to see greater emphasis on educational facilities such as adult education classes, and leisure facilities such as libraries, sports centres and theatres, and on making such facilities more accessible to all sectors of the older population. We are arguing, then, for greater emphasis on flexibility, choice and self-determination, allowing older people to take part in a wider range of normal social, educational, leisure and community activities.

In the interests of 'normalisation' then, we do not consider that older people whose main needs are for social contacts should necessarily be taken away from their homes to spend all day in a centre which they may find stigmatising. The less gregarious people may prefer social contacts on a smaller scale in their own or neighbours' or relatives' homes. Others may appreciate help in travelling to a local pub, restaurant, cinema or bingo hall, or to a hairdressing salon, rather than going to receive meals, entertainment or hairdressing all in the same place, however convenient this may be for service providers. We recognise that such services are highly valued by those who use them, but suggest that other older people may have different preferences and should be allowed to make choices and compensate for their own lacks, with help from transport and support services as necessary.

What type of provision could be made and by whom?
Our review of the current provision of statutory and voluntary day care services has shown that these services have escalated during the past 25 years, and that their expansion is planned to continue (see chapter 4). There is a lack of reliable and consistent statistical data from which to assess the overall level and spread of service provision, particularly in the non-statutory sectors. Examination of the most recent data available revealed uneven geographical distribution and wide variations in the level of provision between authorities, and both within and between types of service. There were also differences in occupancy rates, with reports of both underuse and over-occupation of available places.

The main types of provision were:

1. day hospitals comprising geriatric day hospitals for short-term treatment and rehabilitation where attendance should be time limited, and psychogeriatric day hospitals with no time limit on attendance, providing both short-term and long-term care
2. SSD community-based day centres
3. SSD day care in residential homes
4. voluntary community-based day centres

In all four types there were increasing numbers of joint-financed units especially for elderly mentally ill people. Overlaps and grey areas blurred the distinctions between types of provision. Similar levels of dependence were found in different types of unit. Variations in the rates of new patients at day hospitals showed that short-term rehabilitation, although an aim, was not always achieved in practice.

These findings indicate a mismatch between needs and provision in some areas. Assessment of needs tended to be on an individual rather than an area-wide basis. Individuals were usually assessed only for the service for which they applied or were referred, which meant that they did not always receive the service most suited to their needs. Further, when they were assessed for day care services, they were rarely assessed for other community care services which they might need. Systems of referral, admission criteria and assessment procedures varied between types of provision and service providers. At those day centres where there was little assessment users tended to be fairly mobile and fit. Other centres used assessment as a rationing device. Elderly people needing transport to a day unit were less likely to be admitted than those who could get there independently. Specialist centres had more formal criteria and procedures, and admitted those with demanding physical needs and severe mental disabilities who were often excluded from other day care services and who, without a specialist centre place, were unlikely to receive any day care service. Groups of elderly people for whom separate day care provision seemed preferable were those who were mentally ill or from ethnic minorities.

The findings outlined above support our recommendation that some conceptual distinction should be made between types of day care services and day facilities. There is a strong case for assessment of overall local needs and jointly planned provision of day care services, since these services impinge on one another and cannot be planned in isolation. Individual multi-disciplinary assessment is necessary for the more specialised day care services taking account of other community care services so that people receive the package of care most appropriate to their needs. Assessment and allocation procedures will need to be clarified and understood by all the agencies concerned. The specialised day care service would have the advantage of being more acceptable to older people than the often stigmatised day centre. Just as in day hospitals at present, there would be a legitimate 'health' reason to attend. There does not seem to be a case for assessment for the more informal day facilities to which people currently refer themselves or may be referred by professionals.

The service development which we recommend would keep a balance between strict assessment and the need for flexibility by separating out the day care services which meet assessed needs from the more flexible and informal day facilities for older people in general. We do not propose tightly drawn categories of services nor of users because we recognise that individual needs vary along a continuum. Multi-disciplinary assessment would be the best way of deciding which services met individual needs. The types of day service and facility should, however, be clearly distinguished by those planning and assessing needs for services. We suggest the following types:

Day care services	*Day facilities*
Short term—medical	Social day facilities
Short term—social	Education facilities
rehabilitation	
Long term—social	Leisure facilities
Long term—medical	

This does not imply that people should necessarily be fitted into one or other of these types since they may have a combination of needs and the services offered may comprise several of these components. The system should allow for movement between the services. Some such typology, however, should be a useful aid to discussion of the different services, and some guidance on priorities could be helpful.

Day care services could be offered, as at present, in day hospitals or day centres with properly equipped and accessible premises. The main responsibility for short-term medical treatment and rehabilitation should rest with the geriatric day hospital, and for short-term treatment and longer-term medical maintenance of elderly mentally ill people with the psychogeriatric day hospital. But there is a case for increased medical input from day hospitals or GPs to day care centres in the community when medical care is not the main need and when long journeys to day hospitals are to be avoided. The increase in jointly provided health and social services centres is to be welcomed in the interests of making services more appropriate and more accessible.

Short-term rehabilitation and longer-term social support and relief for carers could be offered in a number of settings such as day centres, residential homes, and other suitable community-based premises or resource centres, by statutory or voluntary agencies, or jointly provided. The private sector is likely to have an increasing role in providing long-term social day care services. Specialist day care services should be offered as at present for those very physically dependent or elderly mentally dependent people with assessed needs for them; some handicapped or mentally infirm people may be assessed as not needing separate provision and may be appropriately placed in the general day care services for older people or mixed groups. Separate services are also indicated at present for elderly people from ethnic minorities whose needs are not met by the traditional model of service. An element of choice for older people in whether they attend separate or integrated services would be desirable.

Day facilities could be offered in many social, educational and leisure settings by statutory, voluntary and private agencies. There is a role for greater responsibility for the education, libraries and recreation departments of LAs in promoting use of facilities by older people and ensuring that those facilities are accessible to all sectors of the population. This may entail making premises physically accessible for people with disabilities, bringing services into the neighbourhood or into day facility venues, or offering transport services to non-medical/welfare venues. Liaison between different LA departments and with the non-statutory sectors and older people themselves would facilitate promoting the use of all types of day facilities by older people. User-led groups for educational and other activities could also be encouraged, on the model of the University of the Third Age.

It is probable that some elderly people will require both day care services and day facilities; consideration should be given to both in devising community care packages. There is no reason why both types of provision should not be offered in the same building. This would be particularly appropriate in rural areas where suitable separate premises for different services may not be available in the locality. The neighbourhood resource centre, which this study showed to be growing in prevalence and whose expansion we would advocate, would be an ideal venue. It could offer day care services, a social club, a lunch club or restaurant, information and advice, and also education, outreach work and neighbourhood projects in which older people could become involved. Such a venue for all sectors of the older population or the local community in general would also be less stigmatising than the traditional model of day centre. Attention should be given, however, to the needs for private space of the residents if such centres are based on residential homes or sheltered housing units.

How could the components of day care services be developed to meet their objectives more effectively?
In the course of our review of currently provided services we examined particular difficulties experienced by service providers and users, and constraints on service developments (see chapter 5).

Where *management of day units* was concerned, systems of line management and professional accountability varied between types of day care service. Day hospitals stressed the importance of the multi-disciplinary team which met regularly and in which all staff had a role. Formal communication systems such as regular staff meetings were less common for day centres than for day hospitals. There had been little participation of SSD management in the running of day centres and day centre staff tended to be professionally isolated. In some areas SSD managers had become more actively involved in the running and development of centres and in stimulating contact between staff in different centres. We welcome this development and recommend more local control by day care staff over their own unit, which would allow them to offer more flexible services tailored to individual needs.

The unsuitability of *premises* was a constraint on development, particularly in the voluntary sector and where localisation of services was planned. Purpose-built or adapted premises, accessible and equipped for people with disabilities, were more common in the statutory sectors. Problems reported concerned lack of rooms and of storage space and inaccessible toilet facilities and, more seriously, totally unsuitable or dilapidated buildings.

Adequate space and flexibility in the use of space were important considerations especially where use of the same premises by different groups was planned. We found a lack of literature on design of day unit premises. One recent study gave design considerations for different types of centre and pointed out, for example, that for care-based centres the implications of various physical and mental disabilities such as poor mobility and confusion should be taken into account.[5] Further specialised guidance and design briefs are needed to help people who are planning new day units.

We recommend as the main long-term aim for premises that all buildings used for day care services and day facilities should be internally and externally accessible and equipped for people with disabilities. Such buildings could be multi-purpose, with health and social services authorities and voluntary agencies sharing premises or providing services jointly. Premises should have enough rooms or subdividable space for separate activities including quiet rest or conversation to take place. In the short term we recommend that the possibility of using existing buildings, adapted if necessary, be explored so that priority may be given to localising services. School buildings where numbers of pupils were decreasing would be one possible addition to the range of community buildings such as residential homes, sheltered housing units, church halls and community centres.

Activities offered in day units have been criticised as undemanding and repetitive. Such activities could be categorised as therapeutic, medical, service and social, and took place in varying proportions in different types of unit. There was low therapeutic input to day centres and even in some day hospitals little actual time was spent on therapeutic activities. Day centres were less geared than day hospitals to individual treatment and therapy. Personal services included health services such as chiropody, care services such as bathing or hairdressing, and advice and information services. Social activities were more diverse in day centres and the most frequent were games, music and entertainment, and discussions. Day centres were used mainly by working-class elderly people.

If the services are to develop in the way we envisage, we recommend an increase in the therapeutic input to day care services, and a broadening of the range of social, cultural and educational activities of interest to men as well as women in both day care services and day facilities. In addition to the introduction of more stimulating programmes, activities should become more flexible so that they can fit in with the individual care programmes of users. Day care units would need equipment, materials and tools for the range of activities envisaged. It would not be cost-effective for every centre to be equipped for every activity. We suggest that local resource centres could build up a stock of equipment and materials to be borrowed by day units in the area.

Adequate numbers of appropriately *trained staff* are essential to the development of services. Low staffing levels were, however, reported. There was a particular shortage of qualified remedial therapy staff. Volunteers played a central role in voluntary agencies' day units; there were sometimes difficulties in recruiting or replacing them. Day hospital staff were more likely than others to have been trained; the day hospital was itself an important training locus. But day centre staff had low status and little training. The training available for them mainly consisted of short courses and in-service training. There was little training for volunteers; this was often considered unnecessary.

The training needs already apparent will increase if services are to become more specialised and individualised. To increase the therapeutic input will require additional therapists, of whom there is a shortage not only in the day care services. Training for paid and voluntary day care service staff should be increased as a priority and will need to take account of the widening of the range of activities and of the personalisation of services. This will entail not only training in skills but in the policy and philosophy behind the changes so that negative staff attitudes do not hinder the development of more individual participation by users in different activities. If the recommendations of the Griffiths report were implemented, there could be training schemes for general 'community carers' to work in different settings including day care services.[6] This would help in increasing cooperation and understanding. There is also a need for more training for day unit organisers, and the development of joint meetings between organisers and staff of neighbouring units. Both SSDs and voluntary agencies such as Age Concern have a role in training day care workers. For volunteers the use of peer trainers would be valuable.

There were wide differences in *costs and levels and sources of funding* between and within types of day care service. There were difficulties in obtaining accurate information on costs. Day hospitals were usually more expensive than other types of day unit. The East Anglia study pointed out that more services and facilities were available in the more expensive units whereas less expensive ones were limited by lack of facilities and part-time opening.[7] Statutory units were funded by the NHS or LA or joint finance. Sources of funding for voluntary agencies' units were grant aid, joint finance, central government schemes, fundraising and donations, and charges. The voluntary sector experienced problems of underfunding and the uncertainty of continuation of funding. Joint projects or partnerships had been set up between statutory and voluntary agencies to provide day care services.

To meet the objectives of extended and personalised activities, adequate resources are needed to provide premises, equipment and trained staff. Day care services should not be seen as a cheap option. The present system of funding voluntary day units with uncertain short-term finance is very unsatisfactory as it inhibits planning and staff recruitment. Recommendations to remedy this situation will have to await the outcome of government consideration of the Griffiths report.[8] The implementation of Griffiths' recommendations would mean that SSDs would have responsibility for funding projects which are currently joint financed, and would have specific grants for community care with which to provide or purchase day care services among other services. Griffiths insisted that community care services should be adequately resourced.

How could services be coordinated?
The present and previous studies found little coordination between day care services and other community care services, between different sectors of day care services, and between service providers and users (see chapter 6). There was, however, a growing recognition of the need for more coordination and joint planning in the development of integrated services for elderly people. Some SSDs had integrated their local management structure for residential, day care, fieldwork and domiciliary services, or introduced localised jointly provided services, for example in resource centres. Joint assessment by health and social services staff, and the use of care managers or key workers to coordinate packages of care for dependent elderly people, were being developed.

Problems arose from a lack of coordination between different sectors of the day care services and a lack of information and understanding about their various functions. Referrals between sectors were thus inhibited and it was difficult to arrange for movement of users from one type of service to another, particularly from day hospitals to day centres. This was partly a result of unplanned provision so that day centres were not always available where required. In recognition of such difficulties joint reviews by statutory and voluntary agencies of the overall day care provision had been carried out in some areas. Solutions they had found included agreed categories of day care service, liaison arrangements and shared or jointly provided services. We have cited examples of good practice in joint community care and day care projects and day resource centres (see chapter 6).

We also found in policy documents a recognition of the need for better communication between day care units and carers of dependent elderly people, and of the need for more information and support for carers. Carers' support groups were being developed and more flexible opening times and weekend cover were being considered.

It is crucial to the development of day care services that they are perceived and planned as part of the range of community care services. We endorse the Griffiths recommendation that SSDs should become lead authorities in organising community care including day care services.[9] All the agencies involved, however, including the growing private sector, should participate in joint committees convened by the SSD to discuss and plan these services.

Joint working by agencies would be an integral part of the development we envisage of day care services tailored to the needs of the individual. We recommend that joint reviews of existing day care services be undertaken as a priority in areas where this has not yet been done. Systems for joint assessment and review for community care and day care services should be introduced. There is scope for increasing joint provision of short-term and long-term day care services, and for greater cooperation and sharing of resources and facilities between day hospitals and day centres. The resource centre model is useful for joint provision and for the integration of day units into the local community.

Where carers are concerned, we suggest that greater attention be paid to their needs, particularly in the introduction of more flexible services with opening times extended to evenings and weekends to suit the schedules of individual carers and their dependents. Reliable information for carers is crucial; they need to know both about other services which could help them, and about the service offered by the unit itself and the particular programme of care for their dependent, in order to play their role in the overall care of the elderly person. Communication between day unit staff and carers should take place not only at review meetings and carers' support groups but should be possible when needed by the carer.

In all types of day unit there is scope for greater participation by both users and carers in the running of the service, although we recognise that not all will welcome such participation and that it can have negative effects. More attention should be paid to the issues of users' and carers' rights and to complaints procedures.

How could transport problems be overcome?
We have identified particular logistical difficulties and shown that transport to day units was perceived as a major problem by all concerned (see chapter 7). The main problems were non-availability or limited hours of availability of transport; shortage of the right type of vehicle, particularly of tail-lift ambulances; staff shortages and lack of cover for absences; difficulties in recruiting volunteer drivers; long journeys; and unpredictability of arrival and departure times. Such difficulties meant limited access to day care places for those most likely to need them, the more disabled and housebound people, and a reduction in the length of time spent at the day unit by those who received transport services.

Approaches to mitigating the effects of transport difficulties were to improve transport services and to reduce the need for them. We identified four categories of improvements to trans-port services; these concerned resources and cost-effectiveness; coordination; administration; and additional sources of trans-port. The need for transport services was reduced by the introduction of travelling and mobile day hospitals and centres, and by localising day care services. The main disadvantage of smaller localised services is that users may not find a compatible companion among a small number of people; the advantages included reduced transport problems, shorter journeys and increased accessibility of services.

We have described the main strategies and administrative measures currently used or considered as ways of reducing transport problems. There is no ideal solution to these difficulties but the various measures suggested could be adopted locally in different combinations, as appropriate to the particular needs of an authority, or preferably considered jointly by the statutory and voluntary agencies offering day care services in a locality.

First, we suggest that agencies attempt to improve transport services by as many as possible of the methods identified. An adequate budget should be secured, numbers of transport places be increased, and the most efficient use be made of resources. A coordinated transport system for the area or some approaches to it could be devised; this should comprise identification of needs and resources, and coordination of use of resources, including the sharing of vehicles. Administrative measures to be considered are zoning, specific vehicles and crew to serve a day unit, and more flexible opening hours and journey times. Different sources of transport should be sought to supplement existing services; examples are voluntary car services, taxis, public minibuses and community transport schemes.

Second, we suggest that the mobile or localised model of service be considered for both day care services and day facilities, particularly in rural areas. Travelling and mobile services are efficient ways of bringing specialised staff, equipment and facilities to a number of different local venues. Two main types are those in which users spend the day in the mobile unit itself, and those which take users and services into existing community buildings. Small day centres in such premises, and resource centres providing day care services as part of a range of flexible services are part of the move towards localisation of services. Another innovation is day care for a very small group of elderly people in the home of a local volunteer.

The localised or mobile model is consistent with our concept of day care services to meet the assessed needs of individuals, which should allow for smaller groupings and a more personalised approach. Day facilities could also be offered on a small, informal, localised basis, which many older people prefer, and which they would find both physically more accessible and more relaxed and welcoming than larger centralised units. The broader range of activities which we advocate would not be precluded by the introduction of small local units if resources were, as suggested above, shared between centres. The localisation of services is also consistent with a more general trend, endorsed by CPA, towards decentralising and de-institutionalising not only care services but also education, leisure and other services.

How could services be monitored and evaluated?
Our study shows that there has been little satisfactory monitoring or evaluation of day care services at any level (see chapter 8). There were few comparative or cost-effectiveness studies which evaluated day care services in comparison with other community care and residential services. Consumer opinion surveys invariably revealed satisfaction, while identifying specific criticisms. For evaluation studies the 'rational' model had been rejected by some researchers in favour of 'pluralistic' evaluation using different perspectives and research methods.

There were four main levels of monitoring and evaluation. At individual user level initial assessment and regular reviews were more likely in day hospitals than other units, but were used by SSDs especially where individual care programmes were concerned. At day care unit level evaluation was by routine monitoring of records and by occasional special studies. We received a few examples of such studies but presume that they were rarely undertaken unless there were problems with a unit, or unless it was part of a specially funded project. Again at area level there was routine monitoring of statistics and special reviews or studies. Since the introduction of the Körner information system more information on day hospitals was available to HAs and to the DHSS.

At national level, statistics were collected annually and used for monitoring. The data however were not satisfactory, particularly for day centres, and little information was available on the voluntary and private sectors. Statistics were used to develop indicators for the assessment of services within a national framework. The limitations of such indicators were recognised. There were few evaluative studies and the research and monitoring undertaken by national bodies was often geared to a particular service rather than providing an overall view. There was no national forum for discussion, research and information, and policy development across the whole spectrum of day care service issues.

Regular monitoring and periodic evaluation at all levels are essential if services are to become more effective and more appropriate to individual users and carers. There should be regular review of individual progress as an integral part of care packages devised to meet individual needs, in order to monitor the effectiveness of the programme, including the contribution of any day care services, and to decide whether any changes are needed. Reliable recording systems are necessary and arrangements for access to and confidentiality of records should be made where joint reviews are concerned.

We also recommend that day care units devise and update reliable and consistent recording systems and monitor these regularly. Consumer opinion should be collected by feedback from workers and groups of staff, and by surveys of users, carers and staff. Occasional evaluation by an outside agency would also be helpful in assessing the effectiveness of services and identifying improvements to be made.

It is essential that at area level LAs and HAs collect adequate basic data on all the services offered by day care units in the area. At the end of chapter 4 we suggest basic items of information to be collected, and at the end of chapter 5 there is a comprehensive summary of the key components of day care services on which data could also be collected and monitored. The SSD or a joint body should take the lead in monitoring and reviewing the overall provision, reassessing needs and identifying trends. We suggest that it is the role of the SSD actively to monitor the day care services provided directly or by voluntary organisations, to give support and guidance, and to encourage development of the services. Consumer opinion and comparative studies on the effectiveness of different services should also be undertaken for the area and it is important that the findings of such studies be disseminated to those involved.

At national level more comprehensive and accurate statistics should be collected and monitored. The introduction of a revised central returns form for day centres to collect more information, including that on the voluntary and private sectors, is a priority. Further refinement of indicator packages and guidance on their use would be helpful, but attention should also be given to the assessment of quality of services, for example by the development of checklists.

The absence of any national forum for day care issues should be remedied. National policy making on day care and monitoring of local services would, of course, be part of the responsibility of a minister for community care as advocated by the Griffiths review.[10] A national body specialising in day care issues would, however, still be necessary. As a precedent we cite the CPA homes advice service leading to a working party and the publication of a code of practice on residential care, *Home life*.[11] We recommend that a national day care advice service be instituted. Such a body could be a resource centre for information and advice for individuals and local and national agencies on day care services; it could undertake or initiate research on day care issues, and disseminate research findings; and it could promote discussion and development of day care services by drawing together policy makers, service providers and professionals from all sectors of service provision.

Finally, as a practical tool for the evaluation and further development of day care services by local statutory and voluntary agencies, we have devised a checklist (see appendix 1) based on the main topics covered by this study. As it includes many items, we suggest that individual units or agencies select those most relevant to compile a checklist for their own purposes.

Further research and development
As chapter 8 has shown, there is a need for major well-designed evaluation studies to ascertain which day care services and aspects of services are most effective in meeting their objectives. Such research should be comparative and include national and local studies of the effectiveness of day care services in a community care context, and cost-effectiveness studies. A longitudinal study showing what happens to older people receiving different forms of day, residential and domiciliary care, and moving between types of care over a number of years, would be particularly valuable. Any further evaluative research should

184

include assessment of consumer opinion including that of non-users, people from ethnic minorities and all social classes.

More specific studies are also needed. Topics for further research are how best to improve the efficiency of transport services, to provide training for day care staff and volunteers, to extend the range of activities offered in day care units, and to help older people to use normal facilities. The methods of joint assessment and review, and in particular the use of computers, software packages, and questions of data protection and confidentiality, would merit detailed attention. In order to stimulate development of more localised, jointly provided and flexible services, experimental projects could be initiated with adequate funding for evaluation. These could include pilot projects where day care units had greater autonomy and a higher level of participation by users and carers than at present.

This study has skimmed the surface of many issues concerning day care services.. Much research remains to be undertaken. We have indicated some directions which may be followed in developing the services. The present ad hoc development cannot be allowed to continue, as resources are not used effectively when services do not reach those who need them most. The profile of day care services must be raised so that they take their due place in policy debates and planning for care in the community.

Our small-scale study is intended to provide a focus for further discussion of and attention to the key issues raised, rather than a definitive view of day care issues. Its contribution to a much needed review of this vital component of the community care services will be heightened if policy makers and service providers at all levels take up the points most relevant to their concerns and pursue them vigorously. The initiation of a national forum for day care issues is, in our opinion, a matter of some urgency. Lack of attention to day care services can no longer be an option.

REFERENCES
1. J. Carter, *Day services for adults—somewhere to go*, George Allen and Unwin, London, 1981
2. G. Fennell, A.R. Emerson, M. Sidell and A. Hague, *Day centres for the elderly in East Anglia*, University of East Anglia School of Economic and Social Studies, Norwich, 1981, p 205

3. Carter, *Day services for adults*, p 135
4. E.M. Goldberg and N. Connelly, *The effectiveness of social care for the elderly*, Policy Studies Institute, London, 1982
5. V. Bacon and M. Dubber, *Buildings used for the day care of elderly people*, Oxford Polytechnic, Oxford, 1987
6. R. Griffiths, *Community care: agenda for action*, HMSO, London, 1988
7. Fennell *et al, Day centres for the elderly*
8. Griffiths, *Community care*
9. Griffiths, *Community care*
10. Griffiths, *Community care*
11. *Home life: a code of practice for residential care*, Centre for Policy on Ageing, London, 1984

Appendix 1:
CHECKLIST FOR THE EVALUATION AND DEVELOP-
MENT OF DAY CARE SERVICES

A. TYPES OF DEFINITIONS AND OBJECTIVES

1. Practical, operational definition of the day care services under consideration.

2. Operational definition for each type of service.

3. Statement of the theoretical or strategic objectives of each service.

4. More detailed statement of specific aims related to the theoretical objectives.

5. Statement of how each aim will be met.

B. BASIC ITEMS OF INFORMATION

1. Definition of the types of day care unit under consideration and the client groups to be catered for in each.

2. Identification of local needs for such provision for different groups of the elderly population, including those with special needs.

3. Comparison of identified needs with current provision.

4. Basic data on the services provided or planned, including the number and location of units, the days open, the number of places per week in each, and attendance figures.

5. Information on the role of each unit, the groups catered for (or excluded), referral and admission criteria and procedures, and transport arrangements, widely available to the different professionals and agencies in the area, as well as to elderly people and carers.

C. COMPONENTS OF DAY CARE SERVICES

1. Management and control
Location of day unit staff within service provider's management structure.
Centralised or local control of individual day care units.
Management committees for individual units.
Administrative responsibility and accountability.
Professional responsibility and accountability.
Key workers for individual users.
Formal communication systems eg. regular meetings.
Participation by users in running units.
Participation by relatives and carers.
Complaints procedures.

2. Premises
Location and ownership of premises.
Purpose-built, adapted or general purpose.
Exclusive or shared use.
External access for disabled people: level access, ramps, rails.
Internal access and circulation space for disabled people.
Environment: decor, furnishings, views, garden.
Flexibility in use of space.
Main activity, sitting, dining and kitchen areas.
Treatment and therapy areas, facilities for chiropody, hairdressing.
Toilet and bathing facilities suitable for disabled people.
Entrance and reception areas, staff offices and facilities, storage space.

3. Activities
Opening hours include early morning/evening/weekend.
Daily/weekly programme of activities.
Programmes for individual users.
Range of intellectual and cultural activities suitable for men and women.
Therapeutic activities eg. occupational and physiotherapy.
Medical treatments and procedures.
Health and personal care services eg. chiropody, bathing, hairdressing.
Advice, information and counselling.
Social activities eg. games, music, discussions, outings.

Meals. Participation by users in preparation.
Availability of drinks and snacks during the day.

4. Staffing and training
Staffing levels adequate to meet objectives.
Roles of paid staff and volunteers.
Availability of professional staff, care staff, organisers and administrative staff, domestic staff, drivers and escorts.
Recruitment of volunteers.
Training for paid and volunteer staff.
Visits and meetings for local day unit staff.
Support and supervision for staff.
Guidance on day unit practice.

5. Costs and funding
Capital costs: buildings and equipment.
Revenue costs: staffing, volunteers' expenses, rent and rates, heating and lighting, administration, catering, transport.
Income from charges to users.
Direct funding of own units by HAs and SSDs.
NHS joint finance.
LA grant aid to voluntary organisations.
Central government-sponsored funding.
Fundraising and donations.

D. TYPES AND LEVELS OF COORDINATION AND COOPERATION

1. Community care and day care

Policy level
Joint planning.
Joint review of policy/service provision.
Jointly agreed procedures.
Communication/information.

Operational level
Joint assessment.
Key workers.
Care packages.
Integrated local services.
Communication/information.

2. Sectors of day care

Policy level
Joint meetings on policy.
Joint planning of provision for locality.
Joint review of policy/provision.
Clarification of roles for each type of service.
Policy on joint funding/grant aid.

Operational level
Referrals/discharge between sectors.
Liaison meetings between and within sectors.
Agreed operational procedures.
Liaison officers.
Input to other services.
Joint training.
Joint project and shared resources.

3. Providers and carers

Policy level
Policy on support for carers.
Identification of needs of carers.
Meeting needs of carers of day care users.
Information for elderly people, carers and workers.

Operational level
Communication between day unit staff and carers.
Involvement of carers as volunteers.
Carers' support groups.
Information for carers and workers.

E. IMPROVING TRANSPORT AND LOCALISING SERVICES

1. Resources and cost-effectiveness
Exploration of all sources of funding, for example joint finance, Help the Aged.
Adequate number of vehicles of appropriate type and size.
Adequate number of drivers and escorts, and arrangements for emergency cover.
Correct number of transport places for people with assessed needs.

Adequate number of day unit staff to cover earlier arrivals and later departures of transport.
Efficient planning of journeys.

2. Coordination
Coordination between transport services in the area.
Coordination between transport services and individual day care units.
Identification of transport needs and resources in the area.
Review of passenger lists.
Transport brokerage—coordination of local resources and needs.
Vehicle sharing by day care service providers.

3. Administration
Zoning—transport for users from same area on same day.
Vehicles specific to day units.
Regular drivers/escorts for the same passengers.
Employment of drivers and escorts in day units during the day.
Use of vehicles for outings, journeys to clinics, shopping.
Flexible opening hours for day units; flexible journey times.
Reliable collection and return times.

4. Additional sources of transport and transport staff
Volunteer car services.
Taxi services.
Volunteer escorts for public transport.
Deregulated public flexible minibus services.
Community transport services.
Dial-a-ride or taxi card schemes.

5. Mobile and localised day care services
Travelling day hospitals/centres.
Mobile day care units.
Small local day centres in existing community buildings.
Rural day centres.
Local resource centres.
Day care by volunteers in private houses.

F. METHODS OF MONITORING AND EVALUATION

1. Individual user level
Initial assessment for day care service.
Regular reviews of progress in day care programme.

Multi-disciplinary assessment for community care services.
Care manager or key worker system.
Regular reviews of success of day care as part of community care.
Multi-disciplinary review meetings.
Detailed records on individual user.

2. Day care unit level

Routine monitoring
Reliable consistent recording system.
Monitoring of attendances, follow-up of non-attenders.
Monitoring of new users and referral sources.
Monitoring and follow-up of leavers.
Monitoring of transport services.
Monitoring of group activities.
Regular staff reviews of unit operation.

Consumer opinion
Self-completion questionnaires for users, carers, staff, other professionals.
Interviews with users, carers, staff, other professionals.
Face to face contact between workers, volunteers and users.
Group discussions for day care staff and other community professionals.

Internal or external evaluation studies by combination of methods
Analysis of records and operational policies.
Interview or assessment and follow-up of users and carers.
Interviews or questionnaires for staff, other community professionals.
Attendance at meetings, carers' groups.
Observation techniques.
Study of costs and cost-effectiveness.
Feedback of findings of evaluation.

3. Local area level

Routine monitoring and review
Recording and monitoring of data on unit places, occupancy and costs.
Updated detailed lists of day care services in area.
Monitoring of transport services and costs.

Monitoring of activities in units.
Guidance to units on how to monitor own services.
Review of day care services and needs by SSD, DHA or
voluntary agency.
Joint review of services by two or more agencies.

Consumer opinion
Self-completion questionnaire for users, carers, staff, other
professionals.
Interviews with users, carers, staff, other professionals.
Group meetings and seminars.

Internal or external evaluation studies by combination of methods
Examination of statistical data.
Interview or assessment and follow-up of users and carers.
Interviews or questionnaires for staff and other professionals.
Attendance at meetings, carers' groups.
Observation techniques.
Comparative studies of units' or sectors' effectiveness.
Comparative studies of costs and cost-effectiveness.
Feedback findings of evaluation eg. day conference and
seminars.

4. National and regional levels
Collection of reliable detailed statistics for all sectors.
Monitoring of authorities' provision.
Development of indicator packages.
In-house or commissioned research.
Comparative studies of effectiveness and cost-effectiveness.
Dissemination of research findings.
National/regional seminars and conferences.